ROTOGRAPHIC
Specialist publishers of price guide reference books. Established 1959

Collectors' Bank Notes Treasury and Bank of England

By Chris Henry Perkins

14th Edition © 2006

INTERNATIONAL STANDARD BOOK No: 0-948964-58-8

A fully updated compilation of averaged selling prices drawn from dealers' lists, auctions, notaphily magazines and websites.

The preceding 2004 12th edition of this book was ISBN 0-948964-68-5.

Most of the illustrated notes in this book are in the possession of the author. Those that are not, are clearly marked as such.

Errors and Omissions:

Every effort has been made to ensure that the information and price data contained within this book is accurate and complete. However, errors do sometimes have a habit or creeping in unnoticed, and with this in mind the following email address has been established for notifications of omissions and errors: omissions@rotographic.co.uk. Readers within the UK can also call the telephone number below.

www.rotogra
0871 87

GW00568313

In Association with F

Contents

Introduction

Welcome to the 14th edition of Collectors' Bank Notes. This edition is the first that I have been involved in, and one of the older type Rotographic titles to be completely updated in terms of layout and style.

Major changes to this edition include entirely new images and a thorough updating of all the price data. The Guernsey overprint notes (pages 34 and 35) have also been updated and re-numbered and the 'Series C' One Pound notes have also been slightly re-numbered with regard to the Goebel machine printed notes.

I admit to being primarily a coin dealer, and the whole task of producing a banknote price guide was incredibly daunting at first. Putting this book together has been a steep learning curve, and this all-new edition would probably not have been possible if it wasn't for the help of the previous author and various other banknote experts. As a thankyou to a couple of those experts, this book is the first ever Rotographic publication to feature advertisements.

I hope you find CBN2006 a worthy successor in the Collectors' Banknotes series.

Chris Perkins (IBNS Member 9299, see page 99 for IBNS membership details)
www.predecimal.com
August 2005

The Layout of this catalogue

As in previous editions, the Treasury notes are dealt with first in spite of the fact that the Bank of England issued notes appeared some two hundred years earlier. Treasury notes were issued for a specific length of time, and because they have an exact start and end point, they are complete. Bank of England notes are still being produced and it is logical therefore to have them after the Treasury notes so that they can be added to as new notes are issued.

Collectors' Banknotes 2006 is therefore laid out in three sections:

The first section covers Treasury Notes printed between 1914 - 1927 including the unofficial Shilling, Half Crown and Five Shillings notes and the Dardanelles campaign overprint notes.

The second section covers Bank of England Notes 1694 - 1928, and includes approximate values for the earlier very rare banknotes where information is available.

The third section covers the modern Bank of England issues, from 1928 - date. This section is naturally fully updated with the new banknote issues each year.

The Layout of the Listings

The listings throughout the book are arranged in six or seven columns. The first column is always the reference number, this number is unique to this book and would have remained unchanged since the first edition (unless stated). New issues are given new reference numbers. The second column is for the date of the Note and the third column will contain the name of the signatory and other relevant variety information. Columns four to seven contain the values of the notes in varying states of preservation (see the introduction to grading on page 4).

Serial Prefix Combinations

At the beginning of most bank note ranges, the serial prefix format is specified along the following guidelines:

LNN = Letter-Number-Number e.g A12
NNL = Number-Number-Letter e.g 12A
LLNN = Letter-Letter-Number-Number e.g AB12
LNNL = Letter-Number-Number-Letter e.g A12B

L/N = Letter over Number e.g $\frac{A}{1}$

L2/N = Letter and small indicated Number over another Number e.g $\frac{L2}{1}$

Other combinations, should they occur will hopefully be quite obvious.

Some note types have either a dot or a dash under the 'No'. Something like: $N^{\underset{\cdot}{o}}$ or $N^{\underline{o}}$

A RADAR number reads the same backwards as it does fowards, e.g 796697.

An Introduction to Bank Note Grading

Grading of Banknotes often comes down to a matter of personal opinion and the ability to grade notes to a degree of accuracy often takes year of experience with different banknote types. Just as with coins, the most common way of grading banknotes is to assign a grade from a range of: Poor, Fair, Fine, Very Fine, Extremely Fine and Uncirculated. Notes that fall between the 'whole' grades are often referred to as 'GVF' (Good Very Fine), 'NEF' (Near Extremely Fine), or even 'AEF' (About Extremely Fine). Only perfect notes in as new condition should be labelled 'Uncirculated'.

For novice collectors a penalty point system has been devised to help with grading. Please note that not all aspects of banknote condition are covered and often the best way to learn how to grade with any degree of accuracy is to befriend an experienced collector or dealer.

Assuming a perfect note is 100%, start at 100 and deduct points based on the following:

Holes	Each pin hole	5 Points
	Larger holes	10+ Points
Edges	Fluffed or uncrisp portions	5 Points
	Tears short of design	10 Points
	Tears reaching into design	20 Points
Folds	Very minor 'Cashiers bend'	2 Points
	Discernable but unsharp fold	5 Points
	Sharp, distinct crease	10 Points
	Several folds (squeezed into small pocket)	20 Points
Dirt/Wear	Area of just noticable discolouration	5 Points
	Grubbiness - Cashiers marks	10 Points
	Partial illegibility from dirt or wear	20 Points

For anything else that makes you less than happy and has not been penalised above deduct: 1 - 5 Points

Range: Up to 15% Poor. 16 - 30% Fair. 31 - 60% Around Fine. Very Fine 75 - 90%. Extremely Fine around 90 - 97% and About Uncirculated (AUNC) between 98 - 99%.

SECTION 1

Treasury Notes 1914 to 1928

The Chancellor of the day, Lloyd George, just a few hours after the midnight Declaration of War, touched on the need to preserve the country's gold. The issue of notes for one pound and for ten shillings were to circulate 'As full as sovereigns and half-sovereigns are current and shall be legal tender in the United Kingdom for the payment of any amount"

The Bank of England felt that large numbers of low-value notes wouldn't be "safe" unless they were printed on special, handmade paper. This meant a relatively slow output. The Chancellor wanted them NOW, so instead, they were produced by the treasury. His announcement in Parliament was on August 5th; Waterlow Brothers and Layton provided the first of the new one pound notes on August 7th! Obviously, there must have been earlier discussions and preparations for such a speedy result. Possibly, a very fine Crystal Ball revealed the inevitability of The Great War.

An astonishing achievement, carried out over a single weekend, saw the printing of a vast number of the new notes. They were printed on ungummed postage stamp paper and carried the G.R. cypher watermark. Bearing the signature of the SECRETARY TO THE TREASURY John Bradbury, the pound notes were printed in black and, appearing just one week later, the ten shilling notes were in red. Both notes were the same size and were printed on only one side of the paper. It was advisable to have all your notes face upwards before counting. Many found face down, it is said, were thrown away as scrap paper! Thomas De La Rue and Company assisted Waterlow Brothers and Layton to produce the ten shilling note. Almost at once, a second series was devised. This time banknote paper was used and a much more elaborate watermark incorporated: the Royal Cypher, value, rose, thistle, shamrock, and daffodil. Still on one side only and in the same colours, some sorting assistance was provided by varying the sizes slightly between the two values. Included in this second series is the issue of: THE DARDANELLES CAMPAIGN Overprints (pages 9 and 13). Third issue "Bradburys", chiefly in brown (£1) and green (10/-) speedily followed, Both sides were printed and the "typical" British banknote was established.

The original purpose of the Treasury note was to gather in the gold. So successful was the exercise that silver was targeted and notes were prepared for five shillings (5/-), half-a-crown (2/6d), and even one shilling (1/-). Fear of runaway inflation through notes unbacked by real assets lead to the destruction of most of these.

Two Shillings and Sixpence
Image used with permission of Pam West Banknotes.

H.M. TREASURY NOTES

(These three not officially issued)

No.	Date	Signature	Fine	VF	EF	UNC

ONE SHILLING

Central vignette of H. M. King George V. Green, brown, white 104x66mm - 4 $^{1}/_{8}$ x 2 $^{5}/_{8}$ in

RT1	1918 (Nov)	**John Bradbury:**				
		A/1 (probably A/1 No. 000000 only)				£6,500
RT2	1919 (Nov)	**N. F. Warren fisher:**				
		L/N B/- (only)		£3,600		

HALFCROWN

(Two Shillings and Six Pence)

Central vignette of H. M. King George V. Olive-green, chocolate and white.

RT3	1918 (Nov)	**John Bradbury:**				
		L/N A/1 No. 000000			£5,000	
	(Auction '96)	Five Colour Trial			£24,000	
RT4	1919 (Nov)	**N. F. Warren-Fisher:**				
		L/N A/-		£4,000		

FIVE SHILLINGS

Central vignette of H. M. King George V. Violet, green and white 5 x 3in -127x76mm

RT5	1917 (Dec)	**John Bradbury:**				
		L/N A/-		£3,300		
RT6	1919 (Nov)	**N. F. Warren-Fisher:**				
		L/N B/-			£3,000	

RT6
Image courtesy of
Pam West Banknotes.

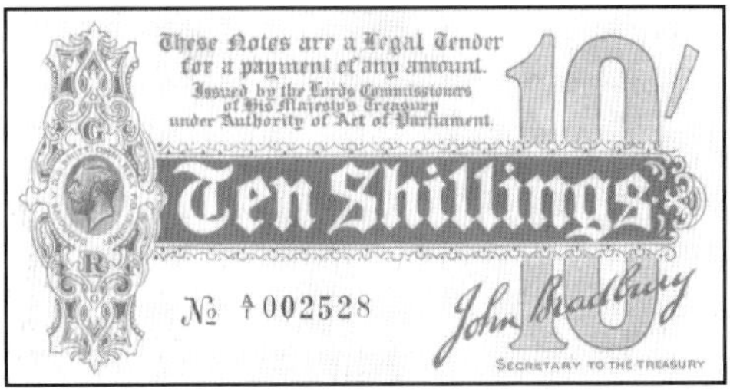

RT8a
Image courtesy of
Pam West Banknotes.

H.M. TREASURY NOTES

TEN SHILLINGS (Type illustrated on previous page)

Small vignette at left - Very large value at right (see picture on previous page)
Red and white - Printed one side only, on stamp paper - 127 x 63.5mm - 5 x 2 $^{1}/_{2}$ in

No.	Date	Signature	Fine	VF	EF	UNC
	1914 (Aug)	**John Bradbury:**				
RT7		L/N - Nº 6 digits (Nº with dot under)				
		S/-		£300	£800	£1200
	(Ireland 2002)	S/- 190137		£350		
	(noted 2002)	T/ "AUNC"				£880
RT8		L/N - Nº 6 digits (Nº with dash under)				
		A/1	£150	£325	£700	£1000
		A/-	£125	£225	£500	£900
	(noted 2005)	A/9				AUNC: £860
RT8a		Variety has no space between prefix and serial (see picture on page 6)				
		A/-			£500	
RT9		L/N - Nº 5 digits (A, B, C possibly other letters, Nº with dot under)				
		B/- •	£150	£900		

TEN SHILLINGS

UNITED KINGDOM OF GREAT BRITAIN AND IRELAND
Red and white, printed only on one side - 136 x 76mm -5 $^{3}/_{8}$ x 3 in
Watermark of wavy lines, Royal Cypher and British Emblems.

No.	Date	Signature	Fine	VF	EF	UNC
	1915	**John Bradbury:**				
RT10		L/N 5 digits - A to M	£80	£140	£350	£600
RT11		L1/N 5 digits - A1 to M1	£35	£105	£300	

RT10

RT11

H.M. TREASURY NOTES

TEN SHILLINGS

UNITED KINGDOM OF GREAT BRITAIN AND IRELAND

Red and white - Printed only on one side - 136 x 76mm - $5\,{}^{3}/_{8}$ x 3 in

Watermark of wavy lines, Royal Cypher and British Emblems

No.	Date	Signature	Fine	VF	EF	UNC
	1915	**John Bradbury:**				
RT12		L2/N A2, B2 or C2 + 5 digits	£80	£225	£400	£600
RT13		L/N plus 6 digits (N to Z)	£80	£175	£275	£400
RT14		L1/N plus 6 digits (O1 to Y1)	£80	£150	£300	£450
	(noted 1999)	S1/62 hand-signed by Versailles Treaty signatorys "torn" £880				
	(noted 2000)	Rounded Shamrock watermark: VF £500 (see RT23b)				

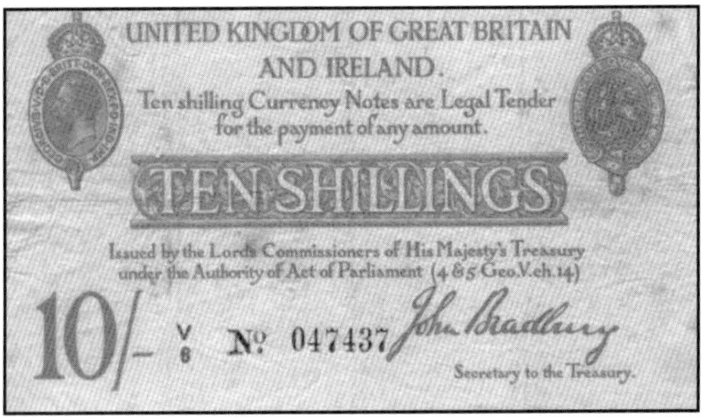

RT13
Image donated

RT14

H.M. TREASURY NOTES
"260 Days"

Under General Sir Ian Hamilton, a force of 30,000 men set sail from Lemnos with the intention of making a landing on the Peninsula of Gallipoli. First ashore, 25th April 1915, were the combined contingents from Australia and New Zealand: the ANZACS. The place of their landing has since been known as Anzac Cove. Getting ashore was relatively easy, but holding the cove in the face of brave and very tough Turkish soldiers, led by Mustafa Kemal (later called Ataturk) brought out the best in the Anzacs who achieved, probably, the only success in a disastrous campaign.

At the tip of the peninsula was Cape Helles. Cape HELL suffices to pinpoint slaughter on a vast scale. Hour after hour the British infantry scrambled down the gang-planks leading from doors cut in the side of the "River Clyde". Most were killed before they even touched the shore. Red ripples washed on to "V" beach. At "W" beach, the 1st Lancashire Fusiliers won their historic "six Victoria Crosses before breakfast" and established a toe-hold at the cost of half their number.

Fierce counter attacks by the Turks eventually reduced all Allied positions to little more than the space they physically occupied. The great Dardanelles Expedition: which was intended to relieve the static, murderous trench warfare of France, itself became the very worst kind of trench warfare where the opposing sides were so close together that hand grenades were tossed from one to the other, and often back again before exploding. The Turks, by digging their trenches so close to their enemy, avoided being shelled by the British fleet. Attacks by the Allies couldn't push back the Turks; massive counter attacks, with huge casualties, couldn't dislodge the Allies, Gallipoli was a disaster.

On the morning of 20th December, the Turks, at first with nervous suspicion, were astonished to find that the entire Anzac force had gone. On the 9th January, the British forces at Cape Helles also "disappeared" in the same way: stealthily, during the night. Both "withdrawals" were brilliantly carried out without casualties.

TEN SHILLINGS - DARDANELLES CAMPAIGN OVERPRINT
Arabic writing in black over RT13)

No.	Signature	Fine	VF	EF	UNC
RT15	**John Bradbury:** L/N plus 6 digits Y/N and Z/N	£350	£600	£950	

Convincing overprint forgeries (on genuine notes) have been seen bearing other than Y or Z serial numbers.

RT15

H.M. TREASURY NOTES

No.	Date	Signature	Fine	VF	EF	UNC
		TEN SHILLINGS				
		Green, purple, brown and white - 138 x 78mm - 5 1/2 x 3 1/8 in				
		Watermark: Royal Cypher - TEN SHILLINGS - four emblems				
	1918 (Oct)	**John Bradbury:**				
RT16		L/N N°. (black with dot under N°)				
		A/N		£200	£400	£600
RT17		L/N N°- (black with dash under N°)				
		A/N	£75	£175	£400	£700
RT18		L/N N°. (red with dot under N°)				
		B/N, C/N	£85	£450	£950	
RT19		L/N N°- (red with dash under N°)				
		B/N, C/N	£85	£125	£250	£550
	1919 (Sep)	**N.F. Warren-Fisher:**				
RT20		L/N N°. (red with dot under N°)				
		D/N	£55	£120	£180	£250
		E/N, F/N, G/N		£100	£170	£240
		H/N		£100	£170	£240

RT19

RT20

RT22

H.M. TREASURY NOTES

No.	Date	Signature	Fine	VF	EF	UNC
		TEN SHILLINGS				
		Green, purple, brown and white - 138 x 78mm - 5 $^1/_2$ x 3 $^1/_8$ in				
		Watermark: Royal Cypher - TEN SHILLINGS - four emblems				
		N.F. Warren-Fisher (continued):				
RT21		L/N N° (red with dash under N°)				
		D/N	£30	£100	£300	£500
		E/N, F/N, G/N	£20	£75	£250	£400
		H/N	£30	£100	£300	£500
RT22		L/N (" N° " omitted. J/- to S/-)				
		J/N and K/N	£30	£100	£250	£450
		L/N to O/N			£250	
		S/N		£100		
	1927 (July)	Now reads "UNITED KINGDOM OF GREAT BRITAIN AND NORTHERN IRELAND"				
RT23a		L/N (as RT22)				
		S/N to W/N	£35	£100	£200	£400
RT23b		The watermark has a mis-shaped shamrock. See below				
		L/12, 32, 52, 72 and 92		£300	£500	

Reverse type common to RT16 - RT23b

RT23b - Watermark: The right shamrock leaf is rounded, not heart shaped, and does not match the other leaves.

H.M. TREASURY NOTES

No.	Date	Signature	Fine	VF	EF	UNC

ONE POUND

Watermark: Royal Cypher, "POSTAGE" - Small vignette at left - very large value at right. Black and White - Printed on one side using postage stamp paper - 127 x 63mm - 5 x 2 $^{1}/_{2}$ in

No.	Date	Signature	Fine	VF	EF	UNC
	1914 (Aug)	**John Bradbury:**				
RT25a.		Capital A. (with stop)	£300	£800	£1500	
RT25b.		Capital B. (with stop)	£225	£500	£1250	
RT2 5c.		Capital C. (with stop)	£350	£750	£1500	
RT26a		Capital A (no stop)	£225	£500	£1250	
RT26b		Capital B (no stop)	£250	£500	£1250	
RT26c		Capital C (no stop)	£250	£500	£1250	
RT27a		L/N N° (with dot under N°) 4 digits		£400	£800	£1400
RT27b		L/N N° (with dot under N°) 5 digits		£350	£800	£1400
RT27c		L/N N° (with dot under N°) 6 digits		£300	£700	£1000
Similar to RT27c		A Trial "W/87 000000" at auction (1994)				£1980
		Colour trial w/mk stars/circles (1998)				£1100
RT27d		L/N N° (with dot under N°) 7 digits		£625	£1250	
RT28a		L/N N° (with dash under N°) 4 digits		£1750		
RT28b		L/N N° (with dash under N°) 5 digits		£600	£950	
RT29a		L/N N° (with dash under N°) 6 small 3mm digits	£500	£1000	£1500	
RT29b		L/N N° (with dot under N°) 7 small digits	£750	£1200		
RT29c		L/N N° (with dash under N°) 6 small 4mm digits	£650	£1000		
RT30		LL/N - 6 digits. BB/-	£200			
		CC/- to LL/- (no II/-)	£100	£300		
RT31		LL/N - No. 4 digits (Stop follows "No") Rare	£1250+	£3000+		

RT27c
Image donated

H.M. TREASURY NOTES

No.	Date	Signature	Fine	VF	EF	UNC

ONE POUND

Watermark: Wavy lines, Royal cypher, ONE POUND and four emblems.
Black and White - Printed on one side using bank note paper - 149 x 85mm - 5 $^{7}/_{8}$ x 3 $^{1}/_{4}$ in

No.	Date	Signature	Fine	VF	EF	UNC
	1914 (Oct)	**John Bradbury:**				
		(Spink 1998) Trial sheet, undated, black and white two notes "small tear". hammer price: £1,100				
RT32		L/N plus five digits (A, with gaps, to Z)		£200	£400	£750
RT33		L1/N plus five digits (A1, with gaps, to L1)	£65	£150	£310	£500

RT32

ONE POUND - DARDANELLES CAMPAIGN OVERPRINT
(see page 9 for 10/- note and more details)
Arabic writing in red over RT32

No.	Date	Signature	Fine	VF	EF	UNC
RT34		**John Bradbury:**				
		F, J, M, P, K, Y	£1000	£2200	£5000	£7000
	(noted 2001)	Repaired, Fine:	£750			

Notes bearing prefixes other than F, J, M, P, K or Y might be genuine notes with fraudulent overprints. Expert advice should be sought.

RT34
Image courtesy of
R J Marles

H.M. TREASURY NOTES

No.	Date	Signature	Fine	VF	EF	UNC

ONE POUND

Watermark: Diagonal lines in alternate bands, ONE POUND and emblems etc.
Brown, purple, green on white or cream paper - St. George and dragon to left
- 152 x 85mm - 6 x 3 $^{3}/_{8}$ in
UNITED KINGDOM OF GREAT BRITAIN AND IRELAND

No.	Date	Signature	Fine	VF	EF	UNC
	1917 (Jan)	**John Bradbury**:				
RT35		L/N (A to H and Z)				
		A/1		£65	£125	£220
		A/-		£40	£95	£150
		B/- to H/-	£20	£40	£85	£110
		Z/-	£15	£35	£85	£125
	1919 (Sep)	**N. F. Warren-Fisher**:				
RT36		L/N (K to Z, without Q and V)				
		K/-		£35	£70	£200
		L/- to Y/-		£38	£60	£170
		Z/-		£38	£75	£190
RT36a		L/N with a much broader 'N°' and a bolder dot. See image below.				
	(Noted)	R/70	£40			

RT36a

RT36, serial with thinner N°
RT36a, serial with broad N° and large dot

No.	Date	Signature	Fine	VF	EF	UNC
	1919 (Sep)	**N. F. Warren-Fisher**: Central watermark				
RT37		L1/N N°. (A1 to R1, without I, Q or Z, round dot under N°)				
		A1/-		£50	£85	£150
		B1/- to R1/-		£20	£75	£100
		Z1/-		£100	£150	£200
RTS37		A1/13 Overprinted 'SPECIMEN' at bottom left and top right				-
RT38		L1/N N°. (with square dot)		£120	£200	£300

H.M. TREASURY NOTES

No.	Date	Signature	Fine	VF	EF	UNC
		ONE POUND				
		Details as previous, but now reads: UNITED KINGDOM OF GREAT BRITAIN AND NORTHERN IRELAND				
	1927 (July)	**N. F. Warren-Fisher**:				
RT39		L1/N N° (S to Z without V and Y, round dot under N°)				
		S1/-	£20	£45	£95	£150
		T1/- to X1/-	£20	£40	£90	
		Z1/-	£30	£65	£125	£200
RT40		L1/N N° (serials as RT39, square dot under N°)				
		S1/- to Z1/-	£60	£130	£200	

RT39

Below: The reverse common to RT35 - RT40

Look out for, and report to Rotographic if an anchor appears here

SECTION TWO:

BANK OF ENGLAND NOTES 1694 - 1928

There were notes even before the Bank of England came into existence in 1694. Gentlemens' agreements in writing were promises (or promissory notes) to reimburse whoever eventually presented the note:

"Thus a note from A to B promising to pay £20 for some shipment would be used by B to pay C for corn. Then A would pay C instead (of B) the original amount of money':

(From D.M. Miller's "Bank of England and Treasury Notes 1694 - 1970").

D.M. Miller also tells how notes for despatch to London were first cut in half and the two halves sent by separate stage coaches to defeat the highwayman. Provided both consignments survived the coach trip, the notes were re-joined, encashed, and cancelled; the cancellation was reinforced by punching or cutting a hole to prevent re-presentation.

The Bank was particularly upset by attempts to forge its notes. Simply being caught in possession of a forgery meant certain transportation. This was harsh when one considers that some forgers were skilled enough to fool bank cashiers. There were so many prosecutions, however, that jurors ignored even the most damning evidence because the punishment was considered too severe. The Bank later endeavoured to ease the situation by arranging for the convict's family to accompany him, and by ensuring that they had some cash upon arrival.

Knowingly possessing a forged note is still an offence. Sending a suspect note to the bank for verification will result in the issue of a Memorandum of Detention if the note proves to be counterfeit; then it will be destroyed. The Bank might well consider that forgeries of notes that are no longer legal tender offer a lesser threat, but in actual fact, Bank of England notes are actually redeemable at the bank for face value indefinitely.

By 1725 there were notes in the range £20, £30, etc, to £100, £200, £300, £400, £500 and £1,000. Notes for £10, £15 and £25 were issued between 1759 and 1765, but none for under £10. Provincial banks and even tradesmen started issuing notes for any sum: in the extreme for one penny! Notes under £5 were eventually prohibited (except in Scotland), but it was too late. Notes issued without sufficient backing assets leads to bankruptcy. Over 100 banks met this fate, and a further 300 eventually closed.

Prosperity brought about by the efforts to pursue the wars with France caused a massive revival of little banks until their number exceeded 700. When war with France was drawing to a close, all the steam went out of the economy and customers found they needed the substance (gold) rather than the promise (notes). Hundreds of banks collapsed and the situation brought even the Bank of England to its knees.

It was found that many would have survived if they could have called-up their cash reserves in time. To remove that difficulty, the Bank of England opened branches to shorten the lines of communication; Birmingham, Bristol, Exeter, Gloucester, Leeds, Liverpool and Manchester branches were followed by others at Belfast, Cardiff, Hull, Leicester, Newcastle, Norwich, Portsmouth, Southampton and Swansea.

Of the bank notes up to, and including Chief Cashier Horace George Bowen, only Henry Hase notes appear with any frequency. Due to the rarity of the 18th and 19th century notes there is insufficient trading to compile useful averages. Only actual offers, or auction results can provide a true guide to value.

BANK OF ENGLAND NOTES 1694 - 1928

Few notes are known to have survived from the period up to Charles Jewson.

The Chief Cashiers 1694 - 1777:
John Kendrick - 1694
Thomas Speed - 1694 to 1699
Thomas Madockes - 1699 to 1739
James Collier with Daniel Race - 1739 to 1751
Daniel Race with Elias Simes - 1751 to 1759
Daniel Race - 1759 to 1775
Charles Jewson - 1775 to 1777

No.	Date	Signature/face value/details	Fine
		Abraham Newland - 1778 to 1807:	
REB1	1797	£1, note No.2, at auction 1993	£57,000
REB2	1798 - 1801	£1, smaller plate, printed signature	£2,000
REB3	1801 - 1803	£1, new watermark, standard size	£1,600
REB4	1803 - 1807	£1, value in watermark	£1,600
REB5	1797	£2, hand written signature	-
REB6	1798 - 1801	£2, smaller plate, printed signature	£6,000
REB7	1801 - 1803	£2, standard size	£4,000
REB8	1803 - 1805	£2, value in watermark	-
REB9	1805 - 1807	£2, new design	£4,000
REB10	1793	£5	£4,500
REB11	1798 - 1801	£10, smaller plate, printed signature	£5,000
REB12	1805 - 1807	£10, Bank of England heading	£6,000
REB13		£15	£7,000
REB14		£20	-
REB15		£100, at auction 2000 (AVF)	£40,250
		Henry Hase - 1807 to 1829:	
REB31		£1, hand written date, countersigned	£2,000
REB32		£1, hand written date, not countersigned	£1,500
REB33		£1, printed date and serials	£800
REB34		£1, emergency issue, dated 1821	£650
REB35		£2, hand written date, countersigned	£4,250
REB36		£2, hand written date, not countersigned	£3,750
REB37		£2, printed date and serials	£2,500
REB38		£5, hand written	£4,600
REB39		£5, printed date and serials	£4,750
REB39T		£5, Trial Hase printed in France, at auction 2000	£1,200

Hase notes were also issued in £10, £15, £20, £25, £30, £40, £50, £100, £200, £300, £500 and £1000 denominations. Very few examples are in private hands. Notes from Bank of England branches other than London were also issued, but, again, are very rare.

BANK OF ENGLAND NOTES 1694 - 1928

No.	Signature/face value/details	Fine
	Thomas Rippon 1829 - 1835:	
REB61	£5	£4,250
REB62	£10	£6,500
	See note under Matthew Marshall section, below.	
	Matthew Marshall 1835 - 1864:	
REB91	£5, hand written signature	£3,250
REB92	£5, printed signature	£3,250
REB93	£5, signature in watermark	£3,250
REB94	£10, hand written signature	£4,250
REB95	£10, printed signature	£4,000
REB96	£10, signature in watermark	£3,250

Marshall and Rippon notes were also issued in £20, £30, £40, £50, £100, £200, £300, £500 and £1000 denominations. Very few examples are in private hands. Notes from Bank of England branches other than London were also issued, but, again, are very rare.

	William Miller 1864 - 1866: (none bear his signature, and the notes are instead signed by the bank officials: W. P. Gattie, T. Kent or C. T. Whitmel)	
REB111	£5, hand written signature	£5,000

During Miller's time as chief cashier notes were also issued in £10, £20, £50, £100, £200, £300, £500 and £1000 denominations. None are known in private hands. Notes from Bank of England branches other than London were also issued, but, again, none are known in private hands.

	George Forbes 1866 - 1873: (Early notes were signed by a bank official and can only be identified as a Forbes by the date)	
REB121	£5, signed by a member of his staff	£3,500
REB122	£5, printed 'Geo Forbes' signature	£6,000
REB123	£10, signed by a member of his staff	-
REB124	£10, printed 'Geo Forbes' signature	£3,500
REB124	£10, as above. VF at auction 2003: £7,000	

Forbes' notes were also issued in £20, £50, £100, £200, £300, £500 and £1000 denominations. None are known in private hands. Notes from Bank of England branches other than London were also issued, but, again, none are known in private hands.

BANK OF ENGLAND NOTES 1694 - 1928

No.	Signature/face value/details	Fine
	Frank May 1873 - 1893:	
REB141	£5	£3,000
REB142	£10	£4,000
	See note under Horace George Bowen section, below.	

No.	Signature/face value/details	Fine	VF
	Horace George Bowen 1893 - 1902:		
REB151	£5	£2,000	£5,000
REB152	£10	£3,000	£4,000

Bowen and May notes were also issued in £20, £50, £100, £200, £300, £500 and £1000 denominations. Very few are known in private hands. Notes from Bank of England branches other than London were also issued, but, again, very few are known in private hands.

No.	Signature/face value/details	Fine	VF	EF
	John Gordon Nairne 1902 - 1918:			
REB160	£1, undated, A/1 000000 serial			£3,000
REB161	£5, London, pre 1911 (1909 noted 2000)		£400	£500
	£5, London, later than 1911		£250	£400
	£5, provincial branches			£600+
REB162	£10, later than 1911		£350	£700
REB163	£20, London or Manchester	£300	£800	£1,600
	Other branches are rare			
REB164	£50, London or Manchester	£250	£500	£1,250
	Other branches			£5,000+
REB165	£100, London or Manchester		£1,000	£2,000
	Other branches are rare			
REB166	£200		£2,500	
REB167	£500		£7,500	
REB168	£1000, Manchester 1911 (Noted 1994)		£12,000	

REB161

REB171

BANK OF ENGLAND NOTES 1694 - 1928

No.	Signature/face value/details	Fine	VF	EF
	Ernest Musgrave Harvey 1918 - 1925:			
REB171	£5, London	£50	£150	£300
	Provincial notes are scarcer, recently noted are:			
	£5, Hull 1919		£500	
	£5, Hull U/96 prefix. Very Good £120			
	£5, Leeds 1919		£220	
	£5, Liverpool			£300
	£5, Manchester 1920		£200	£400
	£5, Newcastle 1919		£350	£600
	£5, Plymouth 1925			UNC: £1,450
REBS171	£5, Specimen 01/Q 0000 (From: Duggleby 6th Edition)			£3,500
REB172	£10, London 1918 - 1922			£400
	£10, London 1923 - 1925			£300
	£10, Newcastle		£300	
REB173	£20	£150	£500	£1750
REB174	£50, Manchester	£300	£700	£1,500
REB175	£100	£450	£900	£1,800
REB176	£200			£1000
REB177	£500		£6,000	
REB178	£1000, very rare			

Early Bank of England notes are found to have one straight cut edge and three untrimmed, or 'torn' edges. The fact they were printed in pairs means that half of them have a left cut edge, whilst the other half have a right cut edge.

BANK OF ENGLAND NOTES from 1928

The Modern Series

In November 1928, under the *Currency and Banknote act* of that year, the Bank of England assumed all responsibility for issuing bank notes. On the 22nd November 1928 the 'Series A' green One Pound notes and red/brown Ten Shilling notes were introduced to circulate with the existing higher denomination white notes (the production of which had not ben affected by the Treasury taking the roll of printing the lower denomination notes). In July 1933 the last of the 10 Shilling and One Pound Treasury notes were withdrawn from circulation.

There was serious intention to replace the silver coins in circulation with notes to the value of One Shilling, Two Shillings, and Five Shillings. The designs for each note were to be identical, front and back, without watermark and not numbered. A thread however, was to be incorporated.

The One Shilling, Two Shilling and Five Shilling notes were not taken beyond the proof stage. Notes for Two Shillings and Sixpence (Half a Crown) and for Five Shillings (a Crown) were produced in large numbers and distributed to a number of banks just in case.

None were put into circulation and they were all recalled to be pulped. However, some of the Half Crown and Crown notes did escape, and are very rare.

One Shilling

Two Shillings

Images on this page used with permission of Pam West Banknotes.

BANK OF ENGLAND NOTES from 1928

No.	Date	Signature/face value/details	VF	EF
		K. O. Peppiatt (1934 - 1949):		
		The Half Crown (Two Shillings and Sixpence) Black on pale blue - 114 x 73mm - 4 $^1/_2$ x 2 $^7/_8$ in Four 2/6 symbols, design the same on both sides		
RB1	1941	No serial numbers	£2,250	£5,250
		Five Shillings (a Crown) Olive green on pale pink - 114 x 73mm - 4 $^1/_2$ x 2 $^7/_8$ in Large central 5, design the same on both sides		
RB2	1941	No serial numbers	£2,250	£5,250

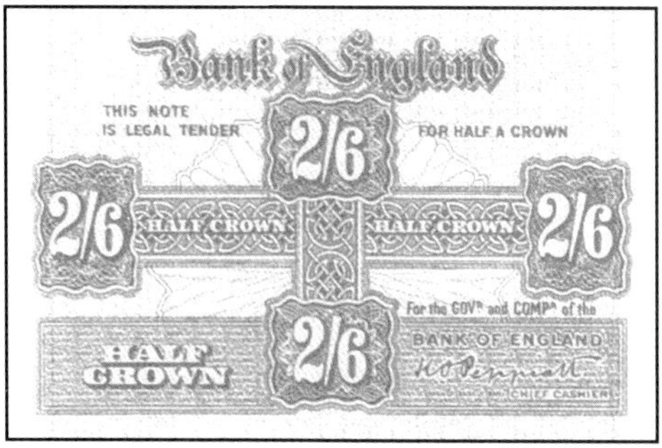

Two Shillings and Six Pence (Half a Crown)

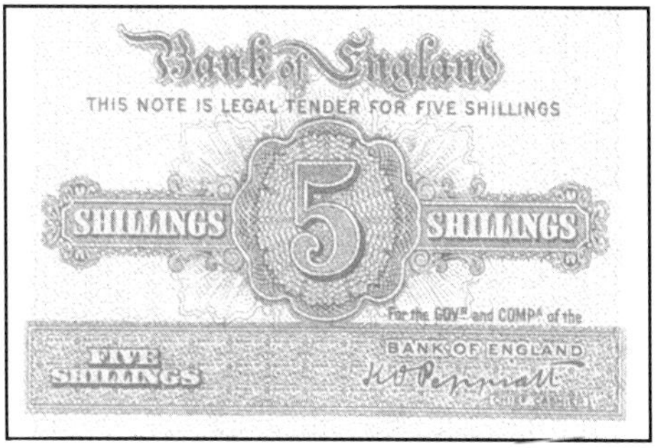

Five Shillings (A Crown)

Images on this page used with permission of Pam West Banknotes.

BANK OF ENGLAND NOTES from 1928

No.	Start date	Signature/face value/details	Fine	VF	EF	AUNC
		Ten Shillings - Britannia type				
		Series A - Red/brown - 137-139 x 78mm - 5 1/2 x 3 1/16 in				
		C. P. Mahon (1925 - 1929):				
RB3	1928 (Nov)	LNN (A , then Z to V backwards)				
		A01	£200	£400	£600	
		Z01	£100	£200	£400	£800
		Z- -		£65	£140	£225
		Y- -, X- -, W- -	£30	£50	£80	£120
		V02 (noted 2000)			£900	
		V- -		£475	£900	
RBS3	1928	A00 000000 SPECIMEN		£1,100 GVF in 2003		
		B. G. Catterns (1929 - 1934):				
RB5	1930 (July)	LNN (V14 to K99 without P)				
		V14	£30	£60	£120	£350
		V- -		£40	£90	£240
		V98 (noted 2003)			£130	
		U- - to L- - (without P)		£15	£50	£170
		K- -		£55	£110	£275

RB5

Reverse common to all from RB3 to RB20 (With subtle tone differences for the Mauve RB10)

BANK OF ENGLAND NOTES from 1928

Ten Shillings - Britannia type (continued)

Series A - **Red/brown** - 137-139 x 78mm - 5 $^{1}/_{2}$ x 3 $^{1}/_{16}$ in

K. O. Peppiatt (1934 - 1949):

No.	Start date	Signature/face value/details	VF	EF	AUNC
RB7	1934 (Oct)	LNN (J01 to A99 without F, G or I)			
		J01	£200	£400	£600
		J- -	£35	£75	£150
		H- - to B - - (without F or G)	£20	£50	£80
		A- -	£35	£75	£150
RBS7		Q00 000000 SPECIMEN (1998)			£1,150
RB8		NNL (01Z to 42O without P, Q, V)			
		01Z	£125	£250	
		- -Z	£25	£65	£90
		- -Y to - -O (without P, Q, V)	£20	£60	£80

RB8

RB10 - Emergency Mauve type (not done justice printed in shades of grey)

Series A - **Mauve** - 137-139 x 78mm - 5 $^{1}/_{2}$ x 3 $^{1}/_{16}$ in
With metal thread, wartime emergency issue.

No.	Start date	Signature/face value/details	VF	EF	AUNC
RB10	1940 (April)	NNL (Z01D to A99D without F, G, I, P, Q or V. Then Z01E to X21E)			
		Z01D	£100	£200	£300
		Z- -D	£20	£35	£70
		Y- -D to B- -D (without F, G, I, P, Q or V)	£15	£30	£60
		A- -D	£20	£45	£75
		No serial number, noted 2002			£320

No.	Start date	Signature/face value/details	VF	EF	AUNC
		Ten Shillings - Britannia type (continued) Series A - **Mauve** - 137-139 x 78mm - $5\,{}^{1}/_{2}$ x $3\,{}^{1}/_{16}$ in With metal thread, wartime emergency issue.			
		K. O. Peppiatt (1934 - 1949):			
RB10	1940 (April)	NNL (Z01D to A99D without F, G, I, P, Q or V. Then Z01E to X21E)			
		Z01E	£30	£60	£110
		Z- -E and Y- -E	£15	£40	£80
		X- -E	£40	£85	£125
		Y23E 343210 (noted 2003) 2 notes with same No.		£200	
		Series A - back to **Red/brown** - 138-140 x 78mm - $5\,{}^{1}/_{2}$ x $3\,{}^{1}/_{16}$ in Without thread in order to use up pre emergency issue paper.			
RB12	1948 (June)	NNL (50O to 70O and then 05L - 71L)			
		- -O		£50	£70
		- -L		£45	£100
RBS12		SPECIMEN	£750	£1,250	
RB14	1948 (Oct)	NNL, as RB12 but **with** security thread. (71L to 91E without F, G or I)			
		71L	£85	£140	£225
		- -K to - -H (without I)	£15	£30	£60
		- -E	£20	£30	£80
RB15		NNL, Replacement notes (01A to 03A)			
		01A	£400	£1000	£1,500
		02A	£200	£500	£750

RB14

No.	Start date	Signature/face value/details	VF	EF	UNC
		Ten Shillings - Britannia type (continued)			
		Series A - Red/brown - 137-139 x 78mm - 5 1/2 x 3 1/16 in			
		P. S. Beale (1949 - 1955):			
RB16	1950 (March)	NNL (92E to 92B)			
		92E	£150	£300	£500
		- -E	£70	£110	£250
		- -D, - -C and - -B	£10	£25	£40
RBS16		SPECIMEN		£1000	
RB17		LNNL (Z01Z to D85Z without F, G, I, P, Q or V)			
		Z01Z	£40	£85	£150
		Z- -Z	£12	£25	£45
		Y- -Z to E- -Z (without F, G, I, P, Q or V)	£5	£20	£40
RB18		Replacement notes (04A - 35A)			
		04A	£300	£800	
		- -A	£75	£120	£250

RB16

No.	Start date	Signature/face value/details	VF	EF	UNC
		L.K. O'Brien (1955 - 1962):			
RB19	1955 (Nov)	LNNL (D86Z to A99Z. Then Z01Y to A99Y without F,G, I, P,Q and V. Then Z01X to Y25X)			
		D86Z	£60	£150	
		D- -Z	£25	£70	£100
		C- -Z to A- -Z	£10	£18	£35
		A99Z	£20	£50	£85
		Z01Y	£45	£85	£170
		Z- -Y	£7	£20	£35
		Y- -Y to A- -Y without F,G, I, P,Q and V	£7	£15	£30
		N- -Y Noted 2001, miscut EF		£150	

No.	Start date	Signature/face value/details	VF	EF	UNC
		Ten Shillings - Britannia type (continued)			
		Series A - Red/brown - 137-139 x 78mm - 5 $^1/_2$ x 3 $^1/_{16}$ in			
		L.K. O'Brien (1955 - 1962) continued:			
RB19	1955 (Nov)	LNNL (Z01X to Y25X)			
		Z- -X	£9	£18	£30
		Y- -X	£15	£30	£65
RBS19		SPECIMEN		£600	£1,125
RB20		Replacement notes (35A to 69A)			
		35A		£300	£750
		- -A	£30	£95	£160

RB19

RB20

Ten Shillings or One Pound - Series B?

The Bank had decided to replace the Series A notes as far back as 1931, but various reasons, including WWII, the Chief Cashier (Beale at that time) not being too struck on the designs, and not to mention a minor disagreement with the designer, delayed their issue. Eventually, in 1957 the only Series B note was issued, being the £5 helmeted Britannia type (see page 55).

BANK OF ENGLAND NOTES from 1928

No.	Start date	Signature/face value/details	Fine	VF	EF	UNC
		Ten Shillings - H.M. The Queen Portrait type				
		Series C - Red/brown - 140 x 66.7mm - 5 $^{1}/_{2}$ x 2 $^{5}/_{8}$ in				
		L.K. O'Brien (1955 - 1962):				
RB21	1961 (Oct)	LNN (A01 to K64 without F, G or I)				
		A01	£15	£30	£75	£150
		A- -	£3	£6	£9	£12
		B- - to J- - (without F, G or I)		£2	£6	£8
		K- -		£5	£10	£20
RBS21		A00 000000 SPECIMEN				£725
RB22		(M01 to M18 replacement notes)				
		M01		£25	£75	£150
		M- -			£25	£35

RB21

Reverse common to all from RB21 to RB28

No.	Start date	Signature/face value/details	Fine	VF	EF	UNC
		J.Q. Hollom (1962 - 1966):				
RB23	1963 (April)	LNN (K65 to Z99 without M, O, P, Q or V)				
		K65		£20	£50	£100
		K- -		£10	£16	£36
		L- - to Y- - without M, O, P, Q or V			£4	£7
		Z- -			£8	£16
		Z98 noted 2003			£12	£22

No.	Start date	Signature/face value/details	VF	EF	UNC

Ten Shillings - H.M. The Queen Portrait type

Series C - Red/brown - 140 x 66.7mm - 5 $^{1}/_{2}$ x 2 $^{5}/_{8}$ in

RB23

RB24

J.Q. Hollom (1962 - 1966):

No.	Start date	Signature/face value/details	VF	EF	UNC
RB24	1963 (April)	NNL (01A to 26R without F, G, I, M, O, P or Q)			
		01A	£25	£65	£110
		- -A	£2	£6	£12
		- -B to - -N without F, G, I, M		£4	£8
		- -R		£18	£32
RB25		LNN (M19 to M55 replacement notes)			
		M19	£10	£20	£50
		M- -	£9	£18	£40
		M55			£100

J.S. Fforde (1966 - 1970):

No.	Start date	Signature/face value/details	VF	EF	UNC
RB26	1967 (Feb)	NNL (26R to 99Z without V)			
		26R Fine: £10	£20	£60	£80
		28R		£15	£35
		- -R		£3	£6
		- -S to - -Y without V		£3	£6
		- -Z		£4	£10
RBS26		SPECIMEN		£750	

BANK OF ENGLAND NOTES from 1928

Ten Shillings - H.M. The Queen Portrait type

Series C - Red/brown - 140 x 66.7mm - 5 $^1/_2$ x 2 $^5/_8$ in

J.S. Fforde (1966 - 1970) continued:

No.	Start date	Signature/face value/details	VF	EF	UNC
RB27	1967 (Feb)	LNNL (A01N to D38N)			
		A01N		£75	
		A- -N	£2	£7	£15
		B- -N and C- -N			£10
		C01N (Coin)		Up to	£20
		D- -N		£4	£10
		D37N			£30
		D38N			£40
RB28		Replacement note LNN (M56 to M80)			
		M56 Fine: £15	£30	£75	£150
		M- -	£3	£5	£10
		M80			£20

RB21 to RB27 feature interesting serial number prefixes, such as: H2O, CO2, O1L, C01N. Interesting spellings sometimes command a small premium.

RB27 with 'COIN' prefix

RB28

BANK OF ENGLAND NOTES from 1928

No.	Start date	Signature/face value/details	Fine	VF	EF	AUNC
		One Pound - Britannia type Series A - Green - 151 x 85mm - 5 $^{15}/_{16}$ x 3 $^{5}/_{16}$ in				
		C. P. Mahon (1925 - 1929):				
RB31	1928 (Nov)	LNN (A01 to H32)				
		A01	£100	£400	£650	£1,300
		A- -	£25	£50	£95	£200
		B- - to G- -		£30	£80	£130
		Presented in parchment envelopes inscribed: 'BANK OF ENGLAND 22 November 1928' were 125 pairs of £1 and 10s notes with matching serial numbers. All are A01 ------	Guestimate		£4,000	£6,000
RBS31		A00 000000 SPECIMEN (noted 1999)				£2,200
		B.G. Catterns (1929 - 1934):				
RB33	1930 (July)	LNN (H33 to Z99 without I, P, Q or V)				
		H33	£20	£60	£150	£300
		H- - to Y- - without I, P, Q or V	£8	£20	£40	£80
		Z- -				£100
		Z99 Higher than above prices, insufficient data				
RBS33		Q00 SPECIMEN			£1,500	
RB34		NNL (01A to 99A)				
		01A	£25	£50	£190	£300
		- -A	£10	£40	£130	£160

RB33

BANK OF ENGLAND NOTES from 1928

No.	Start date	Signature/face value/details	Fine	VF	EF	AUNC
		One Pound - Britannia type (continued)				
		Series A - Green - 151 x 85mm - 5 $^{15}/_{16}$ x 3 $^{5}/_{16}$ in				
		K.O. Peppiatt (1934 - 1949):				
RB36	1934 (Oct)	NNL (01B to 99Z without F, G, I, P, Q or V)				
		01B		£200		
		- -B	£10	£25	£50	£75
		- -C to - -Y without F, G, I, P, Q or V		£10	£20	£35
		- -Z		£20	£45	£70
RBS36		SPECIMEN		£750	£1,500	
RB37		LNNL (A03A to L39A without F, G or I)				
		A01A Not yet seen				
		A03A		£40	£80	£200
		A- -A		£20	£40	£100
		B- -A to K- -A without F, G or I		£9	£18	£55
		L- -A		£20	£40	£70
		L39A		£35	£75	

RB36

RB42 Reverse - Showing the design common to notes RB31 - RB54 (with tone differences, as RB42 was a Blue type)

No.	Start date	Signature/face value/details	Fine	VF	EF	UNC
		One Pound - Britannia type (continued)				
		Series A - **Blue** - 151 x 85mm - 5 $^{15}/_{16}$ x 3 $^{5}/_{16}$ in				
		With a metal thread.				
		K.O. Peppiatt (1934 - 1949):				
RB41	1940 (March)	LNNL (A- -D, A- -E and A- -H)				
		A01D	£10	£55	£120	£200
		A- -D	£3	£15	£30	£55
		A01E	£9	£50	£95	£150
		A- -E and A- -H	£3	£10	£20	£40
		A01H	£4	£12	£20	£40
RBS41		SPECIMEN A00D 000000			UNC:	£1,250

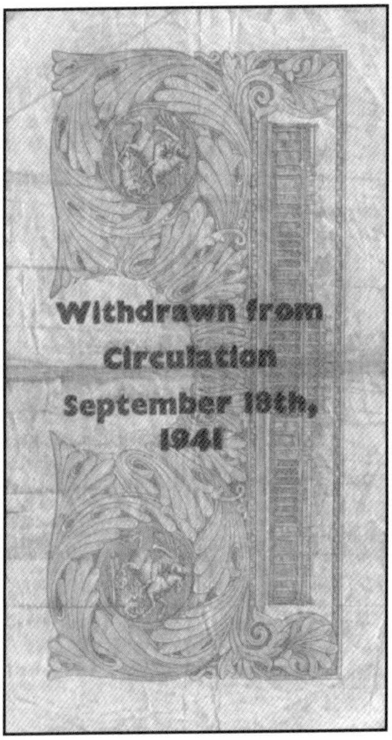

The front and back of Guernsey Overprint note RBG37a. Background information on the next page.

BANK OF ENGLAND NOTES from 1928

One Pound - Britannia type (continued)

The Guernsey Overprint

When the Germans occupied the Channel Islands in WWII almost all the British Channel Island currency was hoarded by the inhabitants. Small change was short, so the Germans gave permission for the islanders to issue small denominations of their own to the total value of £5,000. To prevent potential damage to the economy, this was done subject to the withdrawal and handing over of £5,000 worth of English bank notes to the Germans. After the first £5,000, the islanders were still short of change, so, again, £5,000 of notes were withdrawn and handed to the Germans, and another £5,000 worth of small change was made for use on the island. The notes handed over were old notes that were due to be destroyed, and on both ocassions they were stamped '**Withdrawn from circulation**' with either the date: September 18th 1941, or November 10th 1941.

Please note that the Guernsey overprint section has been re-organised in this edition, and the reference numbers changed to incorporate a 'G' for Guernsey for easy identification. The two digits in the reference number refer to the note type that was overprinted.

No.	Start date	Signature/face value/details	Fine	VF	EF	AUNC
		Guernsey Overprints dated 18 September:				
RBG31a	**Mahon**	A- - to H- - (48 only)		£350	£500	
RBG33a	**Catterns**	H- - to Z- - (69 only)		£325	£475	
RBG34a	**Catterns**	- -A (5 only)		£2,250		
RBG36a	**Peppiatt**	- -B to - -Z (330 only)		£150	£300	
RBG37a	**Peppiatt**	A- -A to L- -A (1,885)		£150	£300	£450
RBG41a	**Peppiatt**	A- -D (35 only) Blue type		£325	£550	
RBG42a	**Peppiatt**	C- -D (85 only) Blue type			£250	£450
		Guernsey Overprints dated 10 November:				
RBG37b	**Peppiatt**	E03A (75 only)		£300	£525	
RBG37c	**Peppiatt**	E15A (403 only)	£125	£250	£325	£425

The suffixes on the reference numbers above refer to the full stop after the overprint:
a: Has full stop after the '1941' on the front only.
b: Has full stop after the '1941' on front and back.
c: Has full stop after the '1941' on the back only

BANK OF ENGLAND NOTES from 1928

No.	Start date	Signature/face value/details	Fine	VF	EF	UNC
		One Pound - Britannia type (continued)				
		Series A - **Blue** - 151 x 85mm - 5 15/16 x 3 5/16 in				
		With a metal thread.				
		K.O. Peppiatt (1934 - 1949):				
RB42	1940 (Sep)	LNNL (B01D to Z87D, B01E to W48E and B01H to X96H without F, G, I, P, Q or V)				
		B01D	£5	£10	£25	£50
		- 01D	£4	£8	£15	£30
		B- -D	£2	£4	£8	£12
		C- -D to Z- -D without F, G, I, P, Q or V		£4	£8	£12
		Z87D, highest number found, so possibly of slightly higher value.				
		B01E	£5	£10	£40	£90
		- 01E	£4	£8	£15	£30
		B- -E	£5	£15	£35	£70
		C- -E to W- -E without F, G, I, P, Q or V		£4	£11	£18
		B01H	£5	£10	£25	£100
		B- -H	£5	£15	£35	£70
		- 01H	£4	£8	£15	£30
		B- -H to X- -H without F, G, I, P, Q or V		£4	£11	£18
RBS42		SPECIMEN A00D		£600	£1,200	
NOTE -		Back to the **Green** type, without the metal thread. Sizes as previous type				
RB44	1948 (June)	LNNL (R01A to S48A)				
		R01A	£10	£45	£90	£180
		R- -A		£20	£40	£75
		S01A	£10	£45	£90	£180
		S- -A		£20	£40	£60

RB42

BANK OF ENGLAND NOTES from 1928

No.	Start date	Signature/face value/details	Fine	VF	EF	UNC

One Pound - Britannia type (continued)

Series A - **Green** - 151 x 85mm - 5 $^{15}/_{16}$ x 3 $^{5}/_{16}$ in
With a metal thread.

K.O. Peppiatt (1934 - 1949):

NOTE - The prefixes of RB44 and RB46 do overlap. The metal thread, or absence thereof are the only means of differentiating these otherwise identical types.

RB46 1948 (Sep) LNNL (S40A to Z99A and A01B to H36B without V, F or G)

	Fine	VF	EF	UNC
S40A	£15	£30	£80	£160
S- -A		£10	£35	£60
S99A (noted 1999)			£75	
T- -A to Y- -A without V		£4	£10	£25
Z- -A	£3	£6	£25	£45
A01B	£10	£20	£40	£100
A- -B			£20	£50
B- -B to H- -B without F or G		£5	£10	£20
H33B to H35B tend to be higher in value, often double H- -B				
H36B	£25	£80		

RB46

RB47 LNNL (S01S to S09S, replacement notes)

	VF	EF
S01S	£150	£350
S- -S	EF:	£150 - £200

BANK OF ENGLAND NOTES from 1928

No.	Start date	Signature/face value/details	Fine	VF	EF	UNC
		One Pound - Britannia type (continued)				
		Series A - Green - 151 x 85mm - 5 15/16 x 3 5/16 in				
		P.S. Beale (1949 - 1955):				
RB51	1950 (March)	LNNL (H37B to Z99B, A01C to Z99C and A01J to L63J without F, G, I, P, Q or V)				
		H37B	£25	£60	£120	£200
		H- -B		£6	£20	£35
		H99B (noted 2003)			UNC:	£60
		- 01B			£10	£20
		J- -B to Z- -B without P, Q or V		£3	£6	£12
		Z98B and Z99B values a little higher				
		A01C	£4	£9	£20	£45
		A- -C		£4	£9	£25
		- 01C		£5	£10	£20
		B- -C to Y- -C without F, G, I, P, Q or V		£3	£5	£7
		Z- -C		£4	£8	£16
		A01J		£10	£20	£40
		A- -J			£8	£25
		B- -J to K- -J without F, G or I		£3	£6	£20
		L- -J		£5	£12	£18
		L63J	£4	£9	£20	£40
RBS51		SPECIMEN			£600	£1,200
RB52		LNNL (S10S to S70S, replacement notes)				
		S10S		£150	£200	£320
		up to S24S		£30	£125	
		S- -S		£8	£20	£50

RB51

RB52 - Serial Number

BANK OF ENGLAND NOTES from 1928

No.	Start date	Signature/face value/details	Fine	VF	EF	UNC
		One Pound - Britannia type (continued) Series A - Green - 151 x 85mm - 5 $^{15}/_{16}$ x 3 $^{5}/_{16}$ in				
		L. K. O'Brien (1955 - 1962):				
RB53	1955 (Nov)	LNNL (L64J to Z99J, A01K - Z99K and A01L to K13L without F, G, I, P, Q or V)				
		L64J		£50	£110	£230
		L- -J to Z- -J without P, Q or V		£4	£12	£24
		- 01 -		£6	£15	£30
		Z99J			£100	
		A01K		£15	£45	£90
		A- -K		£6	£18	£24
		B- -K to Y- -K without F, G, I, P, Q or V		£3	£6	£12
		- 01 -		£4	£6	£12
		Z- -K		£6	£18	£24
		A01L		£30	£60	£120
		A- -L			£20	£40
		A- -L 000007 (or other very low numbers)		£40		
		B- -L to J- -L without F, G or I		£2	£4	£10
		K- -L		£10	£25	£60
		K13L		£20	£40	£80
RBS53		SPECIMEN			£650	£1,200
RB54		LNNL (S71S to S99S and S01T to S23T replacement notes)				
		S71S		£50	£125	£250
		S73S		£15	£30	£60
		S99S			£115	
		S01T		£50	£125	£250
		S- -T			£60	
		S23T			£100?	

RB53

BANK OF ENGLAND NOTES from 1928

One Pound - H.M. The Queen Portrait type

Series C - Green - 151 x 71.8mm - 6 x 2 $^{1}/_{2}$ in
No series B £1 notes were issued, see bottom of page 28.

RB65

RB65 Reverse - Common to all notes RB61 - RB84

No.	Start date	Signature/face value/details	Fine	VF	EF	UNC
		L. K. O'Brien (1955 - 1962):				
RB61	1960 (March)	LNN (A01 to Z99 without F, G, I, M, O, P, Q or V)				
		A01		£50	£100	£175
		A- -		£2	£8	£12
		B- - to Y- - without F, G, I, M, O, P, Q or V			£3	£5
		- 01			£4	£6
		Z- -		£2	£6	£15
RBS61		A00 000000			£1,200 (1998)	
RB62		NNL (01A to 99Z without F, G, I, M, O, P, Q or V)				
		01A		£30	£60	£90
		- -A		£4	£8	£16
		- -B to - -Y without F, G, I, M, O, P, Q or V			£4	£6
		01 -			£5	£10
		- -Z			£8	£16
RB63*		LNNL (A01N, A05N and A06N, experimental notes, with 'R' on reverse.)				
		A01N	£50	£125	£250	

A05N thought to be the rarest of the three prefixes.
* Formerly Number RB63R

BANK OF ENGLAND NOTES from 1928

No.	Start date	Signature/face value/details	Fine	VF	EF	UNC
		One Pound - H.M. The Queen Portrait type (cont) Series C - Green - 151 x 71.8mm - 6 x 2 1/2 in				
		L. K. O'Brien (1955 - 1962):				
RB64	1960 (March)	LNNL (B01N to B76N)				
		B01N			£100	£200
		B- -N			£15	£30
RB65		LNN (M01 to M68, replacement notes)				
		M01	£15	£30	£75	
		M- -			£8	£20
		J. Q. Hollom (1962 - 1966):				
RB66	1963 (Feb)	LNNL (B- -N, C- -N to L- -N, A- -R to L- -R, A- -S to L- -S, A- -T to L- -T, A- -U to L- -U, A- -W to L- -W, A- -X to K- -X and A- -Y without the usual F, G, I and a few other prefixes which were used in the production of RB70)				
		B77N	£15	£40	£100	£150
		B- -N		£20	£40	£75
		C- -N to L- -N without F, G or I		£2	£4	£6
		A- -R to L- -R without F, G or I		£2	£4	£6
		A- -S to L- -S without F, G or I		£2	£4	£6
		A- -T to L- -T without D, F, G or I		£2	£4	£6
		A- -U to L- -U without F, G or I		£2	£4	£6
		A- -W to L- -W without C, F, G or I		£2	£4	£6
		A- -X to K- -X without F, G or I		£2	£4	£6
		A- -Y		£2	£4	£6
		B- -Y		£15	£40	£90
RBS66		SPECIMEN			£750	
RB67		LNN (M68 to M99 replacement notes)				
		M68		£40	£100	
		M- -	£5	£15	£30	£60
RB68		NNL (01M to 99M replacement notes)				
		01M	£15	£40	£85	
		- -M			£10	£30
RB69		LNNL (M01R - M08R replacement notes)				
		M01R				£200
		M- -R			£50	£80

BANK OF ENGLAND NOTES from 1928

No.	Start date	Signature/face value/details	Fine	VF	EF	UNC

One Pound - H.M. The Queen Portrait type (cont)

Series C - Green - 151 x 71.8mm - 6 x 2 $^1/_2$ in

J. Q. Hollom (1962 - 1966):

No.	Start date	Signature/face value/details	Fine	VF	EF	UNC
RB70	1963 (Feb)	LNNL (A- -N, C- -W, D- -T and L- -X) With small 'G' on reverse to indicate that these notes were printed on a Goebel machine.				
		A09N	£5	£10	£25	£40
		A- -N		£3	£8	£20
		C- -W and D- -T		£2	£4	£6
		L- -X		£2	£5	£8
RB71		LNNL (M01N to M28N replacement notes) With small 'G' on reverse to indicate that these notes were printed on a Goebel machine.				
		M01N and M28N			£50	£100
		M- -N			£20	£60

RB72

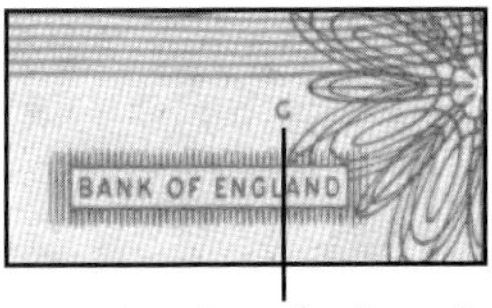

Picture showing the location of the small 'G' on the reverse of the Goebel machine printed notes: RB70, RB71, RB74, RB78 and RB79. The reference numbers previously had a 'G' after them.

J. S. Fforde (1966 - 1970):

No.	Start date	Signature/face value/details	Fine	VF	EF	UNC
RB72	1967 (Feb)	LNNL (B11Y to L- -Y and A- -Z to L99Z without E, F, G and I. A couple of prefixes were used in the production of RB74				
		B11Y		£25	£75	£120
		B- -Y			£15	£30
		C- -Y to L- -Y and A- -Z to J- -Z without letters mentioned above.		£2	£5	£10
		- 01 -		£5	£10	£20
		L- -Z		£6	£12	£25
		L99Z			£30	£50
RB72S		SPECIMEN A00			£750	

BANK OF ENGLAND NOTES from 1928

No.	Start date	Signature/face value/details	VF	EF	UNC
		One Pound - H.M. The Queen Portrait type (cont) Series C - Green - 151 x 71.8mm - 6 x 2 $^1/_2$ in			
		J. S. Fforde (1966 - 1970):			
RB73	1967 (Feb)	LNNL (M09R to M49R replacement notes)			
		M- -R		£25	£50
RB74		LNNL (E01Y to E99Y and K01Z to K99Z) With small 'G' on reverse to indicate that these notes were printed on a Goebel machine.			
		E01Y		£15	
		E- -Y	£2	£4	£7
		K- -Z	£2	£4	£7
		K99Z and perhaps other high numbers	£20	£40	£60
RB75		LNNL (M29N to M42N replacement notes) With small 'G' on reverse to indicate that these notes were printed on a Goebel machine.			
		M29N		£100	£200
		M- -N	£20	£40	£60
		M42N			£160

RB76

No.	Start date	Signature/face value/details	VF	EF	UNC
RB76		LNNL (N01A to X42C without F, G, I, O, P, Q and V) A couple of prefixes were used in the production of RB78. These serials overlap with the early J. B. Page One Pound notes.			
		N01A	£20	£40	£80
		N- -A	£10	£20	£40
		N- -B to N- -L without F, G or I		£4	£6
		R- -A to R- -K without B, F, G or I		£4	£6
		S- -A to S- -L without F, G or I		£4	£6
		S89L (high, usually Page)			£70
		T- -A to T- -L without F, G or I		£4	£6
		U- -A to U- -H without E, F or G		£4	£6
		W- -A to W- -D		£4	£6
		X- -B		£4	£6
		X- -C		£15	
		X10C	£15	£30	£60

BANK OF ENGLAND NOTES from 1928

No.	Start date	Signature/face value/details	VF	EF	UNC

One Pound - H.M. The Queen Portrait type (cont)

Series C - Green - 151 x 71.8mm - 6 x 2 $^1/_2$ in

J. S. Fforde (1966 - 1970):

RB77 1967 (Feb) LNNL (R01M to R53M, S01M to S72M, T01M to T04M and U01M - replacement notes) These serials overlap with the early Page One Pound notes.

	VF	EF	UNC
R- -M	£5	£12	£20
S- -M	£9	£18	£30
T01M	£60	£125	£250
T03M		£150	
U01M		£200	£400

RB78 LNNL (R01B to R99B, R01L to R99L and U01E to U45E) With small 'G' on reverse to indicate that these notes were printed on a Goebel machine.

	VF	EF	UNC
R- -B	£2	£5	£9
R01L			£85
R- -L		£4	£10
R99L			£40
U01E			£120
U45E		£160	

RB78

RB79 LNNL (N01M to N14M, T29 - T32M replacement notes) With small 'G' on reverse to indicate that these notes were printed on a Goebel machine.

N01M			£175?	
N- -M			£20	£55
T- -M	£25	£50	£100	£150
T29M and T32M			£150	

BANK OF ENGLAND NOTES from 1928

No.	Start date	Signature/face value/details	VF	EF	UNC
		One Pound - H.M. The Queen Portrait type (cont) Series C - Green - 151 x 71.8mm - 6 x 2 $^{1}/_{2}$ in			
		J. B. Page (1970 - 1980):			
RB81a	1971	LNNL (S87L, S89L, S90L, T- -B, T- -D to T- -H, T- -K and T- -L, U- -A to U- -D, U- -H, W- -A to W- -H without F or G) Some of the prefix gaps are due to late Fforde notes being assigned them.			
		S87L		£700	
		S89L and S 90L	£100	£350	£700
		T- -B to T- -L without A, C, F, G, I or J		£2	£4
		U- -A to U- -H without E, F or G		£2	£4
		W- -A to W- -H without F or G		£2	£4
RB81b		LNNL (X- -A to Z84L without - - -F, - - -G or - - -I and numbered up to 84 only)			
		X- -A to X- -L without F, G or I		£2	£4
		Y- -A to Y- -L without F, G or I		£2	£4
		Z- -A to Z- -K without F, G or I		£2	£4
		Z- -L	£2	£4	£6
RB82		LNNL (R44M to R99M, S32M to S98M, W01M to W84M, X01M to X60M replacement notes)			
		R- -M			£50
		S- -M	£6	£10	£20
		W- -M	£3	£8	£20
		X01M Noted 2003			£135
		X- -M	£3	£10	£25
		X60M			£70

RB81b

BANK OF ENGLAND NOTES from 1928

No.	Start date	Signature/face value/details	VF	EF	UNC
		One Pound - H.M. The Queen Portrait type (cont)			
		Series C - Green - 151 x 71.8mm - 6 x 2 $^1/_2$ in			
		J. B. Page (1970 - 1980):			
RB83		LLNN (AN01 to HZ63 without O, P, Q or V) Some prefixes are not yet accounted for.			
		AN01	£50	£100	£200
		AN- -	£3	£7	£20
		AN94 Noted 2003			£40
		AR- - to AZ- - without V		£2	£6
		BN- - to BZ- - without O, P, Q or V		£2	£6
		CN- - to CZ- - without O, P, Q, or V		£3	£6
		DN- - to DZ- - without O, P, Q or V		£3	£6
		EN- - to EZ- - without O, P, Q or V		£2	£6
		HN- - to HZ- - without O, P, Q or V	£2	£3	£8
		HU- - 000001			£180
		HZ62		£60	£100
		HZ63		£210	
RB84		LLNN (MR01 to MR41, MS01 to MS84, MT01 to MT23, MU01 to MU18 and MW01 to MW19 replacement notes)			
		MR01 and MS01			£100
		MS84			£90
		MT01			£100
		MU01			£100
		MW01			£100
		MW19			£65
		Others, numbered mid prefix		£6	£12

RB83

BANK OF ENGLAND NOTES from 1928

The replication of Series D and E Bank of England Bank Notes

The Bank of England have given written consent for Rotographic to reproduce its bank notes within this book. To meet the requirements of the Bank of England, with regard to the Series D and Series E notes (covering notes issued between 1971 to date), the word 'SPECIMEN' must appear twice on each note, diagonally, in specified places. So please note that the notes are not Specimen notes unless referred to as such in the text.

One Pound - The Queen / Isaac Newton

Series D - Mainly Green - 134.5 x 66.69mm - 5 $^{5}/_{16}$ x 2 $^{5}/_{8}$ in

RB85

RB85 Reverse - Common to RB85 - RB90, with slight colour enhancements for RB88 - RB90

No.	Start date	Signature/face value/details	VF	EF	UNC
		J. B. Page (1970 - 1980):			
RB85	1978 (Feb)	LNN (A01 to Z80 without F, G, I, M, O, P, Q or V)			
		A01 001205 (low serial)			£60
		A01		£5	£10
		A- -		£4	£6
		B- - to Y- - without F, G, I, M, O, P, Q or V		£2	£4
		Z01	£2	£9	£22
		Z- -	£2	£4	£6
RB85S		SPECIMEN A00 000000			£1000

No.	Start date	Signature/face value/details	VF	EF	UNC
		One Pound - The Queen / Isaac Newton (continued)			
		Series D - Mainly Green - 134.5 x 66.69mm - 5 5/16 x 2 5/8 in			
		J. B. Page (1970 - 1980):			
RB86		LNN (M01 only. Replacement notes)			
		M01		£140	£250
RB87		NNL (01A to 80Y without F, G, I, M, O, P, Q or V)			
		01A		£15	£35
		- -A		£3	£5
		- -B to - -X without F, G, I, M, O, P, Q or V		£2	£4
		01 -		£3	£7
		10U (IOU)			£10
		10W (Isle of Wight)			£6
		- -Y		£4	£6
RB87E		NNL (81E, 81K, 81R, 81S, 81T, 81W, 81X, 81Y experimental. Possibly other prefixes)			
		81E, 81K, 81R, 81S, 81T, 81W, 81X, 81Y		£120	£225
		81Z	£75	£150	£300

RB88 with 'COIN' prefix

No.	Start date	Signature/face value/details	VF	EF	UNC
RB88		LNNL (A01N to E84N)			
		A01N		£20	£50
		A- -N		£5	£14
		B- -N to E- -N		£3	£6
		E84N	£6	£12	£25

BANK OF ENGLAND NOTES from 1928

No.	Start date	Signature/face value/details	VF	EF	UNC
		One Pound - The Queen / Isaac Newton (continued)			
		Series D - Mainly Green - 134.5 x 66.69mm - 5 $^5/_{16}$ x 2 $^5/_8$ in			
		D. H. F Somerset (1980 - 1988):			
RB89		LLNN (A01 to DY21 without O, P, Q or V)			
		AN01			£35
		AN01 000481 Noted 2003			£130
		AR- - to AZ- - without V		£3	£5
		BN- - to BZ- - without O, P, Q or V		£3	£5
		CN- - to CZ- -		£2	£4
		CS22 235689 - Pencilled number with orange stripe See illustration. Fine : £50?			
		DN- - to DX- - without O, P, Q or V		£3	£5
		DY01			£25
		DY21			£35
		The last note produced was DY21 999997, the last 2 digits were spoilt in production. (Source: "Promises to Pay" by Derrick Byatt)			
RBS89		SPECIMEN A00 000000			-
RB90		LLNN (MN04 to MN18, experiemental notes)			
		MN- - Only 6 examples are known	£900	£1,900	£3,500

The £1 coin was introduced in 1983. £1 notes were de-monetized at midnight, March 11th 1988.

RB89

RB89 - CS22 235689 with pencil number and bright orange stripe, presumably to indicate rejection. A replacement note should exist bearing the same number.

BANK OF ENGLAND NOTES from 1928

No.	Start date	Signature/face value/details	Fine	VF	EF	AUNC
		Five Pounds - The 'White Fiver'				
		Black on white - 212 x 135mm - 8 5/16 x 5 5/16 in				
		C. P. Mahon (1925 - 1929):				
RB101	1925 (Apr)	London 1925		£150	£280	£450
		Hull 1927	£300			
		Leeds			£300	
		Liverpool			£375	
		Mahon notes from the following branches also exist: Manchester, Birmingham, Newcastle, Plymouth and Bristol.				
RBS101		SPECIMEN 001/Q			£4,000	
		B.G. Catterns (1929 - 1934):				
RB102	1929 (March)	London 1930			£300	£500
		London 1931		£85		
		London 1932				£500
		Leeds 1929		£275	£395	
		Manchester			£320	
		Liverpool 1931		£275		
		Catterns notes from the following branches also exist: Hull, Birmingham, Bristol, Newcastle and Plymouth.				
RBS102		SPECIMEN			£3,500	

RB102
Image courtesy of Pam West Banknotes.

BANK OF ENGLAND NOTES from 1928

No.	Start date	Signature/face value/details	VF	EF	AUNC
		Five Pounds - The 'White Fiver' (Continued)			
		Black on white - 212 x 135mm - 8 5/16 x 5 5/16 in			
		K. O. Peppiatt (1934 - 1949):			
RB103	1934 (May)	Birmingham		£420	
		Leeds 1937	£260		
		London 1937		£100	
		London 1944		£250	
		Liverpool		£400	
		Newcastle 1937		£580	
		Manchester	£300		
		Hull	£500		
		Notes were also issued in Bristol and Plymouth.			
RBS103		SPECIMEN 000/Q 00000		£3,000	
NOTE		Now with metal thread.			
RB104	1945 (Oct)	LNN (E01 to L02 without F, G or I) Notes dated 1944 exist, although they were not issued until 1945.			
		E01	£100	£160	£300
		E- -		£90	
		H- -, J- - and K- -	£35	£75	£165
		L01 and L02	£125	£225	
RBS104		SPECIMEN E00 000000		£2,000	

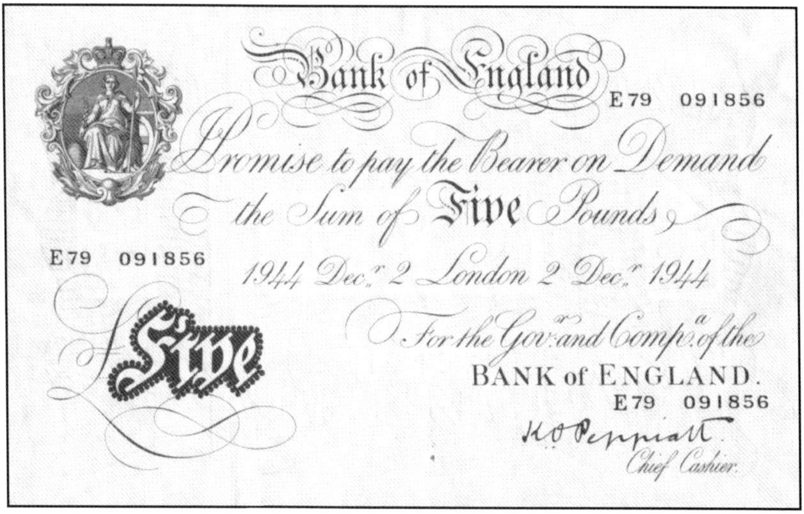

RB104

BANK OF ENGLAND NOTES from 1928

Operation Bernhard - The Nazi White Fivers

In an attempt to damage the British economy, the Nazis forged White Fivers in large numbers. They made one quite noticable 'improvement' to the British watermark, possibly so that they could accurately detect their own forgeries, particularly the top quality ones. Or, perhaps it was a cunning anti Nazi act by the team who laid the wires in the watermarking process. Or, perhaps even nothing more than a slight error. It is the one proven indicator which distinguishes the forgery from the genuine.

The white/clear line in the watermark of the counterfeit notes points to the centre of the triangular serif at the foot of the first 'N' of 'ENGLAND'. In genuine notes the line is off centre and more to the left of the serif when viewed the right way round. In the close-ups below, the 'N' has been magnified and intensified.

Counterfeit Note

Genuine Note

In Issue No.1, Volume 31, of the IBNS Journal there is an article by Lance K. Campbell in which he states quite adamantly that there were no Operation Bernhard (Nazi Forgery) notes for the denominations of £100, £500 or £1000. As always, however, there were other forgers at work. Identifying a forgery does not automatically prove it to be a 'Bernhard' example. The numbers used by the Nazis for the forged £5 notes were as follows:

A/128 to A/175 - A/281 to A/314 - A/317 to A/398
B/105 to B/131 - B/134 to B/182 - B/186 to B/237 - B/256 to B/279
J/373 to J/377

BANK OF ENGLAND NOTES from 1928

No.	Start date	Signature/face value/details	VF	EF	AUNC
		Five Pounds - The 'White Fiver' (Continued)			
		Black on white - 212 x 135mm - 8 5/16 x 5 5/16 in			
		With metal thread, as RB104 but dated 1947.			
		K. O. Peppiatt (1934 - 1949):			
RB105	1948 (Sep)	LNN (L03 to M71)			
		L03	£90	£180	£360
		L- -		£80	£190
		M- -			£165
		M71	£45	£90	£190
RBS105		SPECIMEN			£2,300
		P.S. Beale (1949 - 1955):			
RB106	1949 (Dec)	LNN (M72 to Y70 without Q)			
		M72	£45	£90	£200
		M- -			£165
		N- - to X- - without Q	£40	£75	£165
		X99 Noted 2003		£85	
		Y- -			£200
		Y25		£80	
RBS106		SPECIMEN			£2,500

RB106

BANK OF ENGLAND NOTES from 1928

No.	Start date	Signature/face value/details	VF	EF	AUNC
		Five Pounds - The 'White Fiver' (Continued) Black on white - 212 x 135mm - 8 5/16 x 5 5/16 in			
		L.K. O'Brien (1955 - 1962):			
RB107	1955 (Jan)	LNN (Y71 to Z99)			
		Y71	£45	£100	£150
		Y- -	£30	£75	£100
		Z- -	£25	£65	£85
		Z96	£90	£125	£200
RBS107		SPECIMEN Y71 000000		£1,950	
RB108		LNNL (A- -A to D- -A)			
		A01A	£50	£100	£250
		A- -A	£50	£90	£175
		B- -A to D- -A		£95	£175

RB108

BANK OF ENGLAND NOTES from 1928

Five Pounds - Helmeted Britannia / Lion and Key

Series B - Blue/Green/Orange - 160 x 90mm - 6 $^{5}/_{16}$ x 3 $^{9}/_{16}$ in

See also notes at bottom of page 28 regarding series B.

The two £5 symbols to the left show the difference between notes RB109 and RB110. For RB109 the £5 symbols on the reverse are solid dark blue, with a light thick outline, surrounded by a dark shaded area. In the case of RB110 the £5 symbol is lighter, with a thin dark blue outline surrounded by a darker shaded area.

RB109

RB109 Reverse-Common to RB110 with the exception of the slightly different £5 symbols.

No.	Start date	Signature/face value/details	VF	EF	AUNC
		L.K. O'Brien (1955 - 1962):			
RB109	1957 (Feb)	LNN (A01 to E37) With solid blue reverse £5 symbols (see above).			
		A01		£85	£180
		A- -		£40	£80
		B01, C01, D01 and E01			£60
		B- - to E- -	£10	£25	£50
		E31 Noted 2003		£45	£65
RBS109		SPECIMEN A00 000000			£1,500

BANK OF ENGLAND NOTES from 1928

No.	Start date	Signature/face value/details	EF	AUNC
		Five Pounds - Helmeted Britannia / Lion and Key Series B - Blue/Green/Orange - 160 x 90mm - 6 $^{5}/_{16}$ x 3 $^{9}/_{16}$ in		
		L.K. O'Brien (1955 - 1962):		
RB110	1961 (July)	LNN (H01 to K45 without I) With lighter reverse £5 symbols (see images on page 55).		
		H01	£400	£900
		H- -		£55
		J- -		£50
		K- -	£35	£65
RBS110		SPECIMEN A00 000000	£900	£1,500

RB111 Reverse - Common to notes RB111 to RB118

BANK OF ENGLAND NOTES from 1928

No.	Start date	Signature/face value/details	VF	EF	UNC
		Five Pounds - Queen portrait type			
		Series C - Blue - 140 x 84.8mm - 5 $^{1}/_{2}$ x 3 $^{5}/_{16}$ in			
		Reverse picture on previous page.			
		J.Q. Hollom (1962 - 1966):			
RB111	1963 (Feb)	LNN (A01 to R19 without F, G, I, M, O, P or Q)			
		A01	£50	£100	£170
		A02 and A03		£25	£40
		B- - to N- -		£20	£30
		R- -	£45	£90	£135
RBS111		SPECIMEN A00 000000		£900	
RB112		LNN (M01 to M10 replacement notes)			
		M01	£75	£175	£275
		M- -	£45	£100	£175
		M09		£200	
		J.S. Fforde (1966 - 1970):			
RB113	1967 (Jan)	LNN (R20 to Z99 without V)			
		R20	£30	£85	£180
		R- -	£10	£16	£35
		S- - to Z- - without V		£12	£30
		Z99	£20	£45	£95
RBS113		SPECIMEN A00 000000 (Fforde)		£1000	
RB114		LNN (M08 to M38 replacement notes)			
		M08	£40	£90	£125
		M- -	£30	£110	

RB111

BANK OF ENGLAND NOTES from 1928

No.	Start date	Signature/face value/details	VF	EF	UNC
		Five Pounds - Queen portrait type (continued) Series C - Blue - 140 x 84.8mm - 5 1/2 x 3 5/16 in			
		J.S. Fforde (1966 - 1970):			
RB115		NNL (01A to 40L without F, G or I)			
		01A	£50	£105	£165
		- -A		£15	£40
		- -B to - -K without F, G or I	£9	£12	£30
		- -L	£25	£60	£90
RB116		NNL (01M to 15M replacement notes)			
		01M		£145	
		- -M			£125
		J.B. Page (1970 - 1980):			
RB117	1971	NNL (03C to 40L without F, G or I)			
		03C	£50	£125	£250
		- -C			£75
		- -D to - -L		£20	£55
		40L	£10	£25	£50
RB118		NNL (04M to 18M replacement notes)			
		- -M		£120	£170

RB115

BANK OF ENGLAND NOTES from 1928

Five Pounds - The Queen / Duke of Wellington

Series D - Mainly blue - 145.5 x 77.8mm - 5 $^{3}/_{4}$ x 3 $^{1}/_{16}$ in

To meet the requirements of the Bank of England the word 'SPECIMEN' must appear twice on each series D or E note, diagonally, in specified places. Please also see the top of page 47.

RB121

Reverse - Common to notes RB119 to RB128

No.	Start date	Signature/face value/details	VF	EF	UNC
		J.B. Page (1970 - 1980):			
RB119	1971 (Nov)	LNN (A01 to L94 without F, G or I)			
		A01 0000- - Noted 2003			£300
		A01	£30	£95	£200
		A02		£30	£50
		A- - to K- - without F, G, or I		£10	£20
		L- -	£15	£30	£50
		L94			£125
		Numbers printed on the reverse, Noted 2001 VF: £200			
		No serial number or prefix, Noted 2003 AVF: £160			
RBS119		SPECIMEN A00 000000		£1,250	
RB120		LNN (M01 to M05 replacement notes)			
		M01		£150	£300
		M- -			£150

BANK OF ENGLAND NOTES from 1928

No.	Start date	Signature/face value/details	VF	EF	UNC
		Five Pounds - The Queen / Duke of Wellington			
		Series D - Mainly blue - 145.5 x 77.8mm - 5 $^{3}/_{4}$ x 3 $^{1}/_{16}$ in			
		J.B. Page (1970 - 1980):			
RB121	1973 (Aug)	NNL (01A to 95Z without F, G, I, M, O, P, Q or V) With small 'L' on the back of all, to indicate the printing method used.			
		01A 0000- - Noted 2003			£300
		01A	£45	£85	£180
		- -B to - -Y without F, G, I, M, O, P, Q or V	£8	£15	£30
		94Z			£120
		Printing error with Queen also shown on reverse opposite the Duke Noted 2003			£125
RBS121		SPECIMEN		£1,250	
RB122		NNL (01M to 08M replacement notes)			
		01M		£175	£350
		- -M		£80	£150
RB123		LLNN (AN01 to AZ- -, BN01 to BZ- -, CN01 to CZ- - and EZ04 to EZ56 without O, P, Q or V)			
		AN01	£40	£80	£130
		AN- - to AZ- - without AO, AP, AQ or AV		£12	£20
		BN- - to BZ- - wthout BO, BP, BQ or BV		£12	£20
		CN- - to CZ- - without CO, CP, CQ or CV		£12	£20
		EZ- -		£25	£50
		EZ56	£25	£60	£85

EZ- - also occurs for RB124

RB123

BANK OF ENGLAND NOTES from 1928

No.	Start date	Signature/face value/details	VF	EF	UNC
		Five Pounds - The Queen / Duke of Wellington			
		Series D - Mainly blue - 145.5 x 77.8mm - $5\,^{3}/_{4}$ x $3\,^{1}/_{16}$ in			
		D. H. F. Somerset (1980 - 1988):			
RB124	1980 (June)	LLNN (DN01 to DZ- -, EN01 to EZ- -, HN01 to HZ- -, JN01 to JZ- -, KN01 to KZ- -, LN01 to LZ- - without O, P, Q or V. Also NA- - to NC90)			
		DN01 000154			£250+
		DN01	£40	£75	£100
		DN- -			£30
		DN- - to DZ- - without DO, DP, DQ or DV			£15
		DU- - With no signature (see picture below)		£90	£150
		EN- - to EZ- - without EO, EP, EQ or EV			£15
		EZ58 (Close to Page number)			£35
		HN- - to HZ- - without HO, HP, HQ or HV			£15
		JN- - to JZ- - without JO, JP, JQ or JV			£15
		KN- - to KZ- - without KO, KP, KQ or KV			£15
		LN- - to LY- - without LO, LP, LQ or LV			£15
		LZ- -		£20	£40
		LZ89			£100
		*NA- - to NC- -			£20
		NC01			£30
		NC90			£35

* According to 'English Paper Money' (2002) by Vincent Duggleby (Reference No. B343) the prefix NA01 has not been seen. This casts doubts for me as to its existence. Please let me know if you have information on the NA01 prefix.

No.	Start date	Signature/face value/details	VF	EF	UNC
RB126		LL91 (AN91, BR91, CS91, DT91, EU91, HW91, JX91, KY91 and LZ91)			
		AN91 and BR91 Noted 2003	£550		
		CS91 and KY91 Noted 2003	£300		

RB124 - The type with missing signature.

BANK OF ENGLAND NOTES from 1928

No.	Start date	Signature/face value/details	VF	EF	UNC
		Five Pounds - The Queen / Duke of Wellington			
		Series D - Mainly blue - 145.5 x 77.8mm - 5 3/4 x 3 1/16 in			
		D. H. F. Somerset (1980 - 1988):			
RB127	1987 (July)	LLNN (RA01 to RC90 with thicker security thread)			
		RA01 000763			£100
		RA01		£20	£40
		RA- -, RB- - and RC- -			£18
		RB01 and RC01			£25
		RC90			£70
RBS127		SPECIMEN in Bank of England archives.			-
		G. M. Gill (1988 - 1991):			
RB128	1988 (Mar)	LLNN (RD01 to RL- -, SA01 to SE90 without RF, RG or RI)			
		RD01			£40
		RD- - to RL- - without RF, RG or RI		£10	£20
		SA- - to SE- -		£10	£20
		- -01		£12	£25
		SE90			£80

1500 Wallets containing the 'last' Wellington £5 and 'first' Stephenson £5 with identical serial numbers were issued by the bank and are still available at the time of writing for £110.00 Please also see the information about the special issues on page 65.

RB128

BANK OF ENGLAND NOTES from 1928

No.	Start date	Signature/face value/details	VF	EF	UNC

Five Pounds - The Queen / George Stephenson

Series E - Mainly Green - 135 x 70mm - 5 $^{5}/_{16}$ x 2 $^{3}/_{4}$ in

G. M. Gill (1988 - 1991):

No.	Start date	Signature/face value/details	VF	EF	UNC
RB501*	1990 (June)	LNN (A01 to U17 without F, G, I, M, O, P or Q)			
		A01			£25
		A- - to U- - without F, G, I, M, O, P or Q			£15
		A06 example with differing serials, noted 1999			£100
		Example missing olive green and orange colours.			approx £100
		E67 Pair of consecutive notes missing much detail to the right, with absent Queen. (see below)			approx £250

* Formerly RB129

RB501

RB501 Reverse - Common to notes RB501 - RB510

RB501 Error (The second note of a consecutive pair) - Much detail missing. A very faint outline of The Queen is just about visible.

BANK OF ENGLAND NOTES from 1928

No.	Start date	Signature/face value/details	VF	EF	UNC
		Five Pounds - The Queen / George Stephenson			
		Series E - Mainly Green - 135 x 70mm - 5 $^5/_{16}$ x 2 $^3/_4$ in			
		G. E. A. Kentfield (1991 - 1998):			
RB502	1991 (Nov)	LNN (R01 to W18 without V)			
		R01 0000- -			£150
		R01			£35
		R- - to W- - without V		£7	£25
		W18			£75
		See page 74 for £5 and £10 paired serial numbers. Sets were also sold with matching £5 and £20 notes, and matching £5, £10, £20 and £50 notes.			
RB503		LLNN (AA01 to AB18) As RB502 but with bolder £5 denomination.			
		AA01			£25
		AA- - and AB- -			£12
RBS503		SPECIMEN AA00 000000			£1,125
RB504		LLNN (AC01 to AL- -, BA- - to BL- -, CA- - to CL- -, and DA- - to DC- -, all without -F, -G or -I. Also DL99 which was a special run used only for notes destined for presentation packs) As RB503 but printed using slightly different process.			
		AC01			£70
		AC- - to AL- - without AF, AG or AI		£10	£15
		BA- - to BL- - without BF, BG or BI		£9	£12
		CA- - to CL- - without CF, CG or CI		£8	£10
		DA- -, DB- - and DC- -		£8	£10
RB504b		LLNN (LL01 to LL45 replacement notes)			
		LL- -	£50	£95	£140

RB504

BANK OF ENGLAND NOTES from 1928 - Cypher Notes

Notes with special serial numbers, to mark important occasions.

In a similar fashion to what the Royal Mint and Royal Mail have been doing for some time, in 1988 new opportunities were seen for the exploitation of Bank notes aimed at collectors (or people wanting to buy a gift for a collector!) in order to generate more profit.

In 1990 the first presentation packs were issued containing the 'last' series D and 'first' series E notes with matching serial numbers. At first this venture wasn't very well organised. Prices of the special notes became over inflated and some collectors and dealers were displeased about the way the notes were distributed.

In 1996 special notes started to be issued to mark important occasions, the first being the Queens 70th Birthday. The values of many of these notes now may not be as high as the original issue prices. As with similar 'commemorative' items (often for pretty obscure things!) from the Royal Mint and the Royal Mail, the secondary market is generally much quieter than the market for such items when they are new. This is partly because most of the people that want such items get them when they are new and then keep them. Therefore there are far fewer people looking for them 'second hand'. The fact that some of these special serial number issues were sometimes presented with coins from the Royal Mint, and stamps from the Royal Mail, tends not to affect their desirability.

Five Pounds - The Queen / George Stephenson

Series E - Mainly Green - 135 x 70mm - 5 $^5/_{16}$ x 2 $^3/_4$ in

G. E. A. Kentfield (1991 - 1998):

Cypher Note for the Queens 70th Birthday.
HM70 000001 to HM70 050000 including UNC 1996 £5 Coin.
Issue Price: £39.95

Cypher Note to mark the handing over of Hong Kong back to China
HK97 000001 to HK97 999999 (certain numbers missed out) UNC: £30
HK97 - - - - - - in mini sheet of 12 UNC: £150
HK97 - - - - - - in mini sheet of 35 UNC: £300

Cypher Note to honour the Queen's Golden wedding anniversary
HM50 000001 to HM50 005000 including UNC1997 £5 coin -

Cypher Note for the occassion of reaching 1998!
YR19 980001 to (unsure) -

Cypher Note for Prince Charles 50th Birthday
PW50 000001 to PW50 001000 including 1998 £5 coin.
Issue Price: £39.95

Cypher Note for reaching 1999.
YR19 9900001 to (unsure) -

BANK OF ENGLAND NOTES from 1928

No.	Start date	Signature/face value/details	EF	UNC
		Five Pounds - The Queen / George Stephenson		
		Series E - Mainly Green - 135 x 70mm - 5 $^{5}/_{16}$ x 2 $^{3}/_{4}$ in		
		Merlyn Lowther (1999 - 2003):		
RB507	1998 (Jan)	LLNN (EA01 to EJ45 without F, G or I and also CL01 to CL45)		
		EA01		£25
		EA- - to EJ- - without F, G or I		£10
		EJ45	£20	£40
		CL- - Column Sort		£20
RB508		LLNN (LL01 to LL45 replacement notes)		
		LL- -	£15	£30
RB509	2000	Cypher Note (see previous page) for the Millenium YR20 000001 to (unsure)		-
RB510		Cypher Note for the Queen Mother's 100th birthday QM10 000001 to QM10 010000 with £5 coin and stamp		
		Issue Price:		£60

RB508

No.	Start date	Signature/face value/details	EF	UNC
		Five Pounds - The Queen / Elizabeth Fry		
		Series E - Mainly Green - 135 x 70mm - 5 $^{5}/_{16}$ x 2 $^{3}/_{4}$ in		
		Still series E, similar to previous. Same dimensions and chief cashier, but with a new face on the reverse; that of Elizabeth Fry.		
RB511	2002 (May)	LLNN (HA- -, HB- -, HC- -, DL- -, JA- -, JB- - and XB12)		
		HA01		£15
		HA- -, HC- -, DL- - and JB- -		£8
		JA- - Without missing varnish on serial number		£12
		JA- - With missing varnish on serial number		£16
		JA90 Last prefix, with missing varnish		£30
		DL25 Column sort prefix		£20
		XB12 Varnish trial		£45
RB512		LLNN (LL01 to LL90 replacement notes)		
		LL- -		£15

BANK OF ENGLAND NOTES from 1928

No.	Date	Signature/face value/details	EF	UNC
		Five Pounds - The Queen / Elizabeth Fry Series E - Mainly Green - 135 x 70mm - 5 $^{5}/_{16}$ x 2 $^{3}/_{4}$ in		
RB513	2001	Cypher Note for the Victoria Centenary VR10 000251 to VR10 000650		-
RB514	2002	Cypher Note for the Queen's Golden Jubilee A mini sheet uncut pair of HM02 and HM03		-
		Andrew Bailey (2003 - date):		
RB515		LLNN (JB46 (traced) to JD- -. The JB prefix overlaps with Lowther)		
		JB46		£35
		JB- - to JD- -		£8

RB515

Reverse - Common to RB511 - RB515

BANK OF ENGLAND NOTES from 1928

No.	Start date	Signature/face value/details	Fine	VF	EF	UNC
		Ten Pounds - Large Black and White dated type				
		212 x 135mm - 8 1/4 x 5 1/4 in				
		C. P. Mahon (1925 - 1929):				
RB151	1925 (Apr)	1925 London		£200	£400	
		1925 Liverpool			£400	
		1925 Manchester			£400	
		1927 London			£300	
		1927 Birmingham			£375	
		B. G. Catterns (1929 to 1934):				
RB152	1929 (Mar)	1929 London		£125	£300	£550
		1929 Liverpool		£250		
		1929 Birmingham			£800	
		K. O. Peppiatt (1934 to 1949):				
RB153	1934 (Aug)	1934 London		£150	£300	£500
		1935 London				£500
		1938 London				£650
		1938 Liverpool			£500	
		1935 Birmingham			£450	

Ten Pound notes from the above cheif cashiers also exist from the Leeds, Hull, Newcastle, Plymouth and Bristol braches, but are rare.

RB153
Image courtesy of R J Marles.

BANK OF ENGLAND NOTES from 1928

No.	Start date	Signature/face value/details	VF	EF	UNC
		Ten Pounds - The Queen / Lion holding key			
		Series C - Brown - 150 x 93mm - 5 5/16 x 3 5/8 in			
		J. Q. Hollom (1962 - 1966):			
RB154	1964 (Feb)	LNN (A01 to A40)			
		A01 in leather folder with B of E letter			£1,250
		A01			£65
		A- -		£25	£50
		A40		£85	£120
RBS154		SPECIMEN A00 000000	AUNC		£1,250
		J. S. Fforde (1966 - 1970):			
RB156	1967 (Jan)	LNN (A41 to A95)			
		A41	£75	£95	£160
		A- -		£30	£50
		A95		£80	£150
RBS156		SPECIMEN A00 000000		£1,250	
		J. B. Page (1970 - 1980):			
RB158		LNN (A91 to C90)			
		A91		£1000	
		B- - and C- -	£15	£25	£40
		C90		No data	
RBS158		SPECIMEN B00 000000			£950

RB156 Image courtesy of Banknote dealer Barry Boswell.

BANK OF ENGLAND NOTES from 1928

No.	Start date	Signature/face value/details	VF	EF	UNC
		Ten Pounds - The Queen / Lion holding key Series C - Brown - 150 x 93mm - 5 $^{5}/_{16}$ x 3 $^{5}/_{8}$ in			
		J. B. Page (1970 - 1980):			
RB159	1971	LNN (M01 to M17 replacement notes)			
		M01			£160
		M- -			£50
		M17			No data

RB158
Image courtesy of Pam West Banknotes.

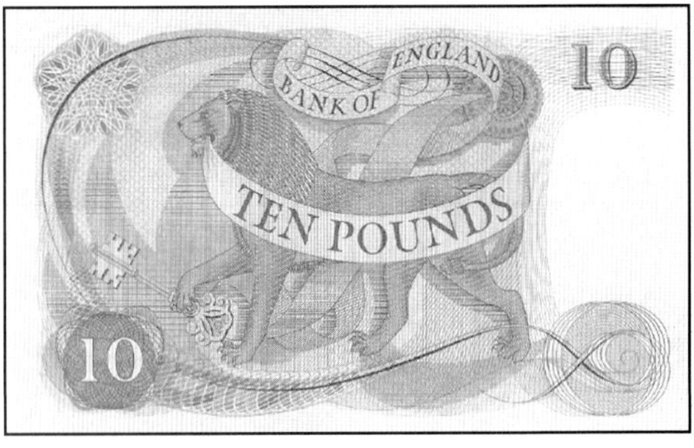

Reverse common to RB154 - RB159
Image courtesy of Pam West Banknotes.

BANK OF ENGLAND NOTES from 1928

Ten Pounds - The Queen / Florence Nightingale

Series D - Mainly Brown - 151 x 84.87mm - 5 $^{7}/_{8}$ x 3 $^{3}/_{8}$ in

To meet the requirements of the Bank of England the word 'SPECIMEN' must appear twice on each series D or E note, diagonally, in specified places. Please also see the top of page 47.

RB167

Reverse common to RB161 - RB168

No.	Start date	Signature/face value/details		VF	EF	UNC
		J. B. Page (1970 - 1980):				
RB161	1975 (Feb)	LNN (A01 to T20 without F, G, I, M, O, P or Q and also U34 and U39)				
		A01			£75	£160
		A- -			£15	£35
		A22 No signature	Approx		£50+	£150+
		B- - to S- - without F, G, I, M, O, P or Q		£15	£20	£25
		U34 and U39 Somerset number note, with page signature in error.				
		U39 - - - - - - at auction in 1999				£632
RBS161		SPECIMEN A00 000000				£1,600
RBS161b		SPECIMEN (without the word overprinted) A00 000000				-

BANK OF ENGLAND NOTES from 1928

No.	Start date	Signature/face value/details	VF	EF	UNC
		Ten Pounds - The Queen / Florence Nightingale			
		Series D - Mainly Brown - 151 x 84.87mm - $5\,^{7}/_{8}$ x $3\,^{3}/_{8}$ in			
		J. B. Page (1970 - 1980):			
RB162	1975 (Feb)	LNN (M01 to M50 replacement notes)			
		M01	£60	£120	£200
		M- -			£150
		M50	£35	£100	£200
		D. H. F. Somerset (1980 - 1988):			
RB163	1980 (Dec)	LNN (U01 to Z80 without V)			
		U01	£200	£400	£600
		U- -		£30	£75
		W- - to Y- -		£15	£25
		Z- -		£20	£70
		Z80		£50	£120
RB164		NNL (01A to 40L without F, G or I)			
		01A		£80	£160
		- -B to - -K without F, G or I		£25	£45
		- -L		£35	£50
		40L		£50	£80
RB165	1984 (Feb)	LLNN (AN01 to CR90 without -O, -P, -Q or -V) With small 'L' on reverse to indicate printing method.			
		AN01		£85	£175
		AN- - to AZ- - without O, P, Q or V		£15	£35
		BN- - to BZ- - without O, P, Q or V		£15	£35
		CN- - and CR- -		£15	£35
		CR67			£60
		CR90		£75	£180
RB166	1987 (July)	LLNN (CS01 to DN30 without CV- -) As RB165 but now with intermittent security thread (Stardust).			
		CS01		£40	£80
		CS- - to CZ- - without CV- -		£15	£30
		DN- -		£18	£36
		DN30		£30	£60

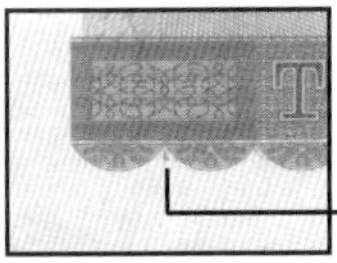

The small 'L' on the reverse of later series D £10 notes to indicate that they were printed using offset photo-lithography.

BANK OF ENGLAND NOTES from 1928

No.	Start date	Signature/face value/details	VF	EF	UNC
		Ten Pounds - The Queen / Florence Nightingale			
		Series D - Mainly Brown - 151 x 84.87mm - 5 7/8 x 3 3/8 in			
		G. M. Gill (1988 - 1991):			
RB167	1988 (Mar)	LLNN (DR01 to DZ- -, EN01 to EZ- -, HN01 to HZ- -, JN01 to JR60 without -O, -P, -Q or -V)			
		DR01		£25	£45
		DR- -			£35
		DS- - to DZ- -without DV- -			£30
		EN- - to EZ- - without EV- -			£30
		HN- - to HZ- - without HV- -			£30
		- -01			£35
		JN01		£15	£40
		JN- -		£40	£75
		JR- -			£65
		JR60			£225
		G. E. A. Kentfield (1991 to 1998):			
RB168	1991 (Nov)	LLNN (KN01 to KN?? and KR01 to KR30)			
		KN01 Low serial			£120
		KN- -			£45
		KR- -			£25
		KR30	£40	£60	£90

BANK OF ENGLAND NOTES from 1928

No.	Start date	Signature/face value/details	EF	UNC
		Ten Pounds - The Queen / Charles Dickens Series E - Mainly Orange - 142 x 75mm - 5 $^{9}/_{16}$ x 2 $^{15}/_{16}$ in		
		G. E. A. Kentfield (1991 - 1998):		
RB1001	1992 (Apr)	LNN (A01 to X40 without F, G, I, M, O, P, Q or V and also Y41 to Y96)		
		A01 First 400		£95
		A01		£35
		A- - to X- - without F, G, I, M, O, P, Q or V	£15	£30
		X40		£80
		Y- -		£45
		Y96	No data	
		£10 series D and Series E with matched serials (Issue price new in March 2005)		£110

RB1003

RB103 Reverse - Common to all from RB1001 to RB1006d

No.	Start date	Signature/face value/details	EF	UNC
RB1002		'Reclaimed' / 'B' Ream notes. Unspoilt notes cut from partially spoilt sheets and separately numbered. Duggleby lists M01 to M40 and Z- - up to Z90		
		M- - and Z- -	£30	£60
		Z90		£75

BANK OF ENGLAND NOTES from 1928

No.	Start date	Signature/face value/details	EF	UNC

Ten Pounds - The Queen / Charles Dickens

Series E - Mainly Orange - 142 x 75mm - 5 $^{9}/_{16}$ x 2 $^{15}/_{16}$ in

G. E. A. Kentfield (1991 - 1998):

RB1003	1993 (Nov)	LLNN (DA01 to DL- -, EA01 to EL- -, H01 to HK- -, JA01 to JK- -, KA01 to KK80 and also K99. Without -F- -, -G- - and -I- -) Now with bolder '£10' symbol on the left, and a second £10 symbol added to the right hand corner of the obverse and reverse.		
		DA01	£60	
		DA- - to DK- - without DF, DG, or DI	£12	£25
		EA- - to EK- - without EF, EG or EI	£12	£25
		DL- - and EL- - (column sort)	£20	£35
		HA- - to HK- - without HF, HG or HI	£12	£20
		JA- - to JK- - without JF, JG or JI	£12	£20
		KA- - to KK- - without KF, KG or KI	£12	£20
		KK99 special run for presentation pack		£45
RB1003b		LLNN (LL01 to LL40 replacement notes)		
		LL- -	£35	£70

Cypher Notes - See page 65

RB1004		Cypher Note for the Queens 70th Birthday. HM70 000001 to HM70 002000 including UNC 1996 Silver proof £5 Coin.	Issue Price: £97.50	
RB1004b		Cypher Note to honour the Queen's Golden wedding anniversary HM50 000001 to HM50 001500 including UNC1997 Silver proof £5 coin	Issue Price: £97.50	
RB1004c		Cypher Note for the occasion of reaching 1998. YR19 980001 to (unsure)		-
RB1005		Cypher Note for Prince Charles 50th Birthday PW50 000001 to PW50 000500 including 1998 Silver proof £5 coin.	Issue Price: £97.50	
RB1005b		Cypher Note for reaching 1999. YR19 9900001 to (unsure)		-

BANK OF ENGLAND NOTES from 1928

No.	Start date	Signature/face value/details	EF	UNC
		Ten Pounds - The Queen / Charles Dickens Series E - Mainly Orange - 142 x 75mm - 5 9/16 x 2 15/16 in		
		Merlyn Lowther (1999 - 2003):		
RB1006	1999 (Jan)	LLNN (KL01, EL- -, KL- -, LA- - to LA80)		
		KL01		£22
		EL01	£20	£40
		EL- -	£15	£30
		KA- - and LA- -	£12	£22
		LA80		£45
		Kentfield/Lowther notes with matched serial numbers (Issue Price)		£55
RB1006b		LLNN (LL01 to LL40 replacement notes)		
		LL- -	£25	£50
		Cypher Notes - See page 65		
RB1006c		Cypher Note for the Millenium. YR20 000001 to YR 001500		-
RB1006d		Cypher Note for the Queen Mother's 100th Birthday QM10 000001 to QM10 000750 including UNC 2000 Silver proof £5 coin		-

BANK OF ENGLAND NOTES from 1928

Ten Pounds - The Queen / Charles Darwin

Series E - Mainly Orange - 142 x 75mm - 5 $^{9}/_{16}$ x 2 $^{15}/_{16}$ in

The design has been changed now on both sides (still series E). Charles Darwin now replaces Charles Dickens on the reverse, the '£10' symbols have been changed and a hologram has been incorporated.

RB1008

RB1008 Reverse - Common to notes RB1007 to current note, at time of writing

No.	Start date	Signature/face value/details	EF	UNC	
		Merlyn Lowther (1999 - 2003):			
RB1007	2000 (Nov)	LLNN (AA01 to AH80 and EL- - without - F or - G. Also some - L prefixes) Copyright claim worded 'The Company' see page 78			
		AA01 007- - -		£35	
		AA01		£30	
		AA- - to AH- - without AF or AG		£20	
		EL- - Column sort			£25
RB1007b		LLNN (LL01 to LL40 replacement notes) Copyright claim worded 'The Company' see page 78			
		LL- -	£35	£70	

No.	Start date	Signature/face value/details	EF	UNC

Ten Pounds - The Queen / Charles Darwin

Series E - Mainly Orange - 142 x 75mm - 5 $^{9}/_{16}$ x 2 $^{15}/_{16}$ in

The copyright claim on the obverse and reverse of notes RB1007 and RB1007b reads (incorrectly) 'THE GOVERNOR AND THE COMPANY OF THE BANK OF ENGLAND', as shown above in the left hand example. Notes from RB1008 onwards read correctly 'THE GOVERNOR AND COMPANY OF THE BANK OF ENGLAND' as shown in the right hand example.

Merlyn Lowther (1999 - 2003):

No.	Start date	Signature/face value/details	EF	UNC
RB1008	2000 (Nov)	LLNN (AA01 for presentation packs, AD- -, AJ- -, AK- -, and BA- - to CC40) Copyright claim worded 'And Company' see above.		
		AA01		£50
		AD- - Overlap prefix	£12	£22
		AJ- - and AK- -		£15
		BA- - to CC- -		£15
		EL- - Column sort	£15	£20
RB1009		LLNN (LL01 to LL40 replacement notes) Copyright claim worded 'And Company' see above.		
		LL- -	£12	£30

Cypher Notes - See page 65

No.	Start date	Signature/face value/details	EF	UNC
RB1010		Cypher Note for the Victorian era Centenary QV10 000001 to QV10 050000 Plus UNC £5 coin		-
RB1010b		Cypher Note for the Victorian era Centenary VR10 000251 to VR10 000950 Plus Silver proof £5 coin		-

BANK OF ENGLAND NOTES from 1928

No.	Start date	Signature/face value/details	EF	UNC
		Ten Pounds - The Queen / Charles Darwin		
		Series E - Mainly Orange - 142 x 75mm - $5\,^{9}/_{16}$ x $2\,^{15}/_{16}$ in		
		Andrew Bailey (2003 - date):		
RB1011		LLNN (CC41 (traced) to CJ- -, without -F, -G or -I)		
		CC41		£20
		CC- - to CJ- - without CF, CG or CI		£15
RB1012		LLNN (LL- - replacement noteds)		
		LL- -		£25

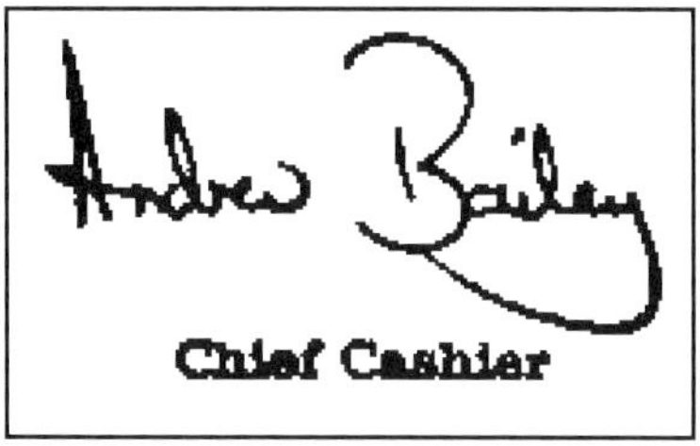

The signature of Cheif Cashier Andrew Bailey

BANK OF ENGLAND NOTES from 1928

No.	Signature/face value/details	VF	EF	AUNC

Twenty Pounds - Black and White type

Serial number large at upper right and repeated smaller lower right
212 x 135mm - 8 $^{5}/_{16}$ x 5 $^{5}/_{16}$ in

These three are rarely encountered. Valuations without market movements are estimates. Valuations presume London notes; branch notes will attract a substantial premium.

RB171	**C. P. Mahon (1925 - 1929):**	£650	£1,250	
RB172	**B. G. Catterns (1929 - 1934):**	£425	£850	
RB173	**K. O. Peppiatt (1934 - 1949):**	£450	£925	

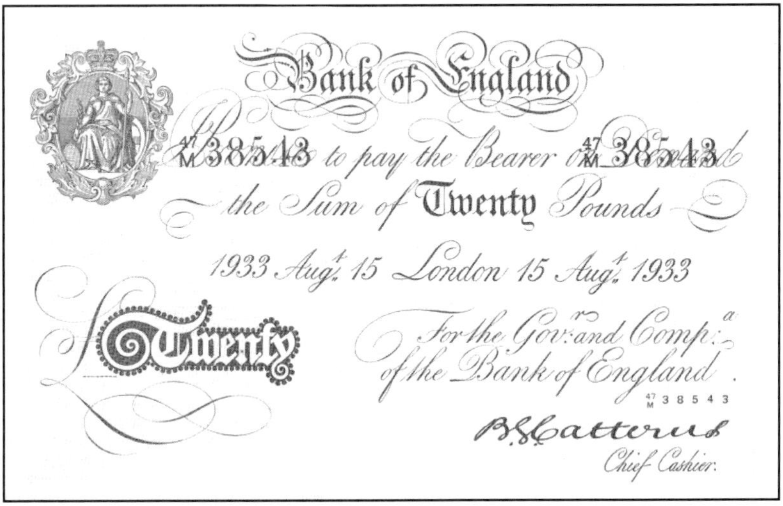

RB172
Image courtesy of Pam West Banknotes.

BANK OF ENGLAND NOTES from 1928

No.	Start date	Signature/face value/details	VF	EF	UNC
		Twenty Pounds - The Queen / Shakespeare Statue Series D - Mainly Purple - 160 x 90mm - 6 1/4 x 3 1/2 in Watermark is an image of The Queen.			
RB174	1970 (July)	**J. S. Fforde (1966 - 1970):**			
		LNN (A01 to A05)			
		A01	£80	£160	£250
		A- -			£140
RBS174		SPECIMEN A00 - - - - - -		£1,500	
RB175		LNN (M01 only, replacement notes)			
		M01	£80	£180	£250
RB176	1970	**J. B. Page (1970 - 1980):**			
		LNN (A06 to D80)			
		A06	£80	£150	£225
		A- -			£80
		B- - and C- -			£60
		D01		£45	
		D- -		£30	£50
RB177		LNN (M01 to M04 replacement notes)			
		M01	£60	£150	£300
		M02 and M03			£210
		M04		£150	£300

RB180 Reverse - Common to notes RB174 to RB181

BANK OF ENGLAND NOTES from 1928

No.	Start date	Signature/face value/details	VF	EF	UNC
		Twenty Pounds - The Queen / Shakespeare Statue Series D - Mainly Purple - 160 x 90mm - 6 1/4 x 3 1/2 in			
RB178	1981 (Mar)	**D. H. F. Somerset (1980 - 1988):**			
		LNN (E01, H- - and J- - to J40)			
		E01	£100	£200	£400
		E02		£120	
		E- -		£50	£90
		H- - and J- -		£50	
		J40		£50	£80
		No prefix or serial numbers			£250
RBS178		SPECIMEN A00 - - - - - -	Estimate		£2,000

RB180

No.	Start date	Signature/face value/details	VF	EF	UNC
RB180	1984 (Nov)	Watermark changed to image of Shakespeare and stardust (dotted) security thread introduced.			
		NNL (01A to 40K without F, G or I)			
		01A 000605		£150	
		01A			£100
		- -A to - -K without F, G or I		£30	£70
		40K		£60	£60
RBS180		SPECIMEN		£1,250	

BANK OF ENGLAND NOTES from 1928

No.	Start date	Signature/face value/details	VF	EF	UNC
		Twenty Pounds - The Queen / Shakespeare Statue			
		Series D - Mainly Purple - 160 x 90mm - 6 1/4 x 3 1/2 in			
RB181	1988 (Mar)	**G. M. Gill (1988 - 1991):**			
		NNL (01L to 20X without O, P, Q or V)			
		01L	£30	£65	£115
		- -L to - -W without O, P, Q or V		£35	£70
		- -X			£100
		20X			£150
		Various errors noted:			
		40S Uncut base, with colour bars			£200
		Extra paper at bottom left			£175
		Numbers upside down			£400
		22R Missing much detail on both sides			£400
RB181 with RB128		£5 Series D SE69 and £20 Series D 20U			£100

RB181

No.	Start date	Signature/face value/details		EF	UNC
		Twenty Pounds - The Queen / Michael Faraday			
		Series E - Mainly Purple - 149 x 80mm - $5\,^{7}/_{8}$ x $3\,^{1}/_{8}$ in			
RB2000*	1991 (June)	**G. M. Gill (1988 - 1991):**			
		LNN (A01 to U19 without F, G, I, M, O, P)			
		A01 early serial (up to 1000)			£75
		A01			£60
		A- - to U- - without F, G, I, M, O or P			£50
		£20 Series D and £20 Series E with matching serials (Issue price)			£195
RB2000b*		LNN (Z13 only. Special purpose notes)			
		Z13	Estimate		£2,000
		*RB2000 was formerly numbered RB182.			
		*RB2000b was formerly numbered RB183.			
RB2001		The 'B' Ream notes - Unspoilt notes taken from partly spoilt sheets and separately numbered. These prefixes are outside of the normal range (all above -70, others would be impossible to identify).			
		A78		£50	
		A91		£60	
		B84	£20		
		B90			£70
RB2001b		LNN (M01 to M31 and Z01 to Z90 with gaps) Experimental notes with prefixes outside the normal range.			
		M01 to M31 with gaps		£40	£80
		Z01 to Z90 with gaps		£35	£70

Reverse - Common to notes RB2000 to RB2004

No.	Start date	Signature/face value/details	EF	UNC
		Twenty Pounds - The Queen / Michael Faraday		
		Series E - Mainly Purple - 149 x 80mm - 5 $^{7}/_{8}$ x 3 $^{1}/_{8}$ in		
RB2002	1991 (Nov)	**G. E. A. Kentfield (1991 - 1998):**		
		LNN (E01 to W35 without F, G, I, M, O, P, Q or V. Later, old stock of prefixes A71 to A99, B71 to B99 and C71 to C99 were used)		
		E01 001- - -		£145
		E- -		£65
		A- -, B- - and C- -	£40	£80
		A71		£200
		E- - to L- - without F, G or I	£40	£80
		N- - to W - - without O, P, Q or V	£25	£50
		W35 999- - - (Noted 2002)		£130
		- 01		£50
		X- - and Y- - Possibly exist, printed on old stock		
RB2002b		LNN (M01 to M31 and Z01 to Z90. Special purpose)	£35	£80
RB2003	1993 (Sep)	LNN (X01 to Y70)		
		As above but with minor design changes: The crown at the top right of the obverse has been replaced with a '£20' symbol, and the left '£20' symbol has been emboldened. On the reverse a '£20' symbol has been added to the top right, and the '£20' at the left is of a different style.		
		X01 0010- -		£70
		X- -		£35
		Y01		£50
		Y- -		£30
		Y70 VF: £60 (Noted 2002)		
RB2003b		Cypher Note for 1998 - YR19 98- - - -		-
RB2004	1994	LLNN (AA01 - AL- -, BA- - to BL- -, CA- - to CJ- - without -F, -G or -I and also CL- -)		
		AA01		£160
		AA- - to AL- - without AF, AG or AI	£25	£45
		BA- - to BL- - without BF, BG or BI	£25	£35
		CA- - to CJ- - without CF, CG or CI	£25	£35
		CL-01 - CL40	£28	£35
		CL99 used in presentation packs only		£50
		Error with mismatched serials, noted 2001		£145
RB2004b		LLNN (LL01 to LL40 replacement note)		
		LL01 - LL40	£40	£80
RB2004c		Cypher Note for 1999 - YR19 99- - - -		-

BANK OF ENGLAND NOTES from 1928

No.	Start date	Signature/face value/details	EF	UNC
		Twenty Pounds - The Queen / Michael Faraday		
		Series E - Mainly Purple - 149 x 80mm - 5 7/8 x 3 1/8 in		
RB2004	1999 (Jan)	**Merlyn Lowther (1999 - 2003):**		
		LLNN (DA01 to DA80)		
		DA01		£70
		DA- -	£35	£55
		DA80		£95
		Twenty Pounds - The Queen / Edward Elgar		
		Still Series E - Mainly Purple - 149 x 80mm - 5 7/8 x 3 1/8 in		
RB2005	1999 (June)	LLNN (AA01 to AL- -, BA01 to BK- - and CA01 to CJ- - without -F, -G or -I. Also DB- - (which was actually the first run to be printed) to DE- -)		
		AA01	£25	£40
		AA- - to AK- - without AF, AG or AI		£25
		AL- - Column sort prefix		£30
		BA01 to BK- - without BF, BG or BI		£25
		CA01 to CJ- - without CF, CG or CI		£25
		DB- - to DE- - (traced to DE80, overlaps with Bailey)		£25

RB2005

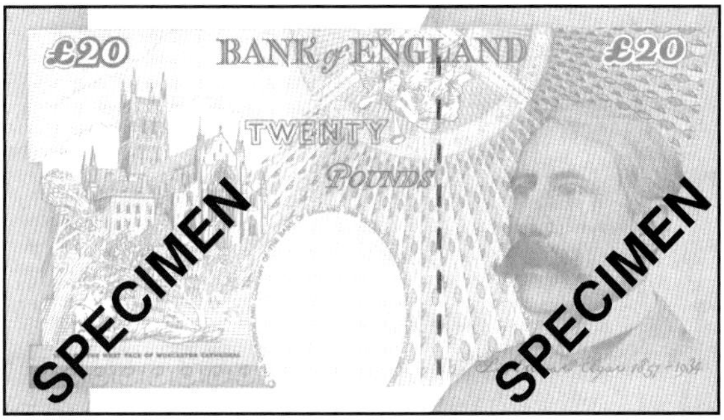

Reverse - Common to notes RB2005 to date

BANK OF ENGLAND NOTES from 1928

No.	Start date	Signature/face value/details	EF	UNC
		Twenty Pounds - The Queen / Edward Elgar Still Series E - Mainly Purple - 149 x 80mm - 5 7/8 x 3 1/8 in		
RB2006b	1999 (Jan)	**Merlyn Lowther (1999 - 2003):**		
		LLNN (LL01 to LL40 replacement notes)		
		LL01	£25	£50
		LL- -	£25	£45
RB2007		Cypher Note for the Millenium - YR20 00- - - - Also sold with Silver Crown		-
RB2008		Cypher Note for Queen Mothers 100th - QM10 00- - - - Also sold with Gold Proof Crown		-
RB2009		Cypher Note for 2001 - YR20 01- - - -		-
RB2010		Cypher Note for the Queens Jubilee		
		With silver proof Crown. Issue price:		£100
		With gold proof Crown. Issue price:		£875
RB2011		Cypher Note for Queens coronation - QC50 - - - - - - -		
		With Silver Crown. Issue price:		£99.50
		With gold proof Crown. Issue price:		£875
RB2012		**Andrew Bailey (2003 - present):**		
		LLNN (DE41 (traced) to DJ- - without -F, -G or -I with Lowther overlaps in the DE- - range)		
		DE- -		£30
		DF- - to DJ- -		£25

RB2012

BANK OF ENGLAND NOTES from 1928

No.	Start date	Signature/face value/details	VF	EF	AUNC
		Fifty Pounds - Large White Type Design on one side only - 212 x 135mm - 8 5/16 x 5 5/16 in			

RB193
Image courtesy of Pam West Banknotes.

No.	Start date	Signature/face value/details	VF	EF	AUNC
		C. P. Mahon (1925 - 1929):			
RB191			£600	£1,200	
		B. G. Catterns (1929 - 1934):			
RB192		London	£400	£800	
		Manchester	£450	£1,250	
		K. O. Peppiatt (1934 - 1949):			
RB193		London	£375	£600	
		Liverpool (Noted 2001) "Backstamped"			£750

BANK OF ENGLAND NOTES from 1928

No.	Start date	Signature/face value/details	VF	EF	UNC

Fifty Pounds - The Queen / Sir Christopher Wren

Series D - Multicoloured - 169 x 95mm - 6 $^5/_8$ x 3 $^3/_4$ in

RB194

No.	Start date	Signature/face value/details	VF	EF	UNC
RB194	1981 (Mar)	**D. H. F. Somerset (1980 - 1988):**			
		LNN (A01 to B90)			
		A01			£200
		A- - and B- -			£130
		B90		£75	£150
		B90 With high serial number			£175
RBS194		SPECIMEN		£1,250	
RB195	1988	**G. M. Gill (1988 - 1991):**			
		LNN (C01 - D90, plus higher D- -, see below)			
		C01	£60	£120	£240
		C- - and D- -		£75	£140
		D90	£65	£100	£150
		Some D- - and E- - prefixes of Gill exist. These notes were issued to replace spoilt Kentfields.			
		D95		£100	
RB196	1991 (Nov)	**G. E. A. Kentfield (1991 - 1998):**			
		LNN (E01 to E30)			
		E01			£150
		E02 000006 (Noted 2003)		AUNC	£165
		E- -			£100
		E30			£150
		E30 With High Serial			£200

Reverse - Common to RB194 - RB196

No.	Start date	Signature/face value/details	EF	UNC
		Fifty Pounds - The Queen / Sir John Houblon		
		Series E - Mainly Red- 156 x 85mm - 6 $^{3}/_{16}$ x 3 $^{5}/_{16}$ in		
RB5001	1994 (Apr)	**G. E. A. Kentfield (1991 - 1998):**		
		LNN (A01 to H- - without F- - or G- -. Also H99 and L- -)		
		A01 001000 or lower		£150
		A01		£110
		A- - to H- - without F- - or G- -		£90
		H99 From presentation packs only		£100
		L- - Column sort prefix	£75	£130
		L35 (highest recorded)	£75	£150
RB5001b		LLNN (LL01 to LL35 column sort notes)		
		LL- -	£75	£120

RB5004

BANK OF ENGLAND NOTES from 1928

No.	Start date	Signature/face value/details	EF	UNC
		Fifty Pounds - The Queen / Sir John Houblon		
		Series E - Mainly Red- 156 x 85mm - 6 $^{3}/_{16}$ x 3 $^{5}/_{16}$ in		
RB5002	1994 (Apr)	**G. E. A. Kentfield (1991 - 1998):**		
		LNN B Ream serials, see note for RB2001		
		A99	£75	£110
		C01		£100
		D94		£140
RB5002b		LNN (M- - experimental notes)		
		M01	£150	£300
		M- -	£130	£250
		M99	£150	£300
RB5003		Cypher Note for Prince Charles' 50th - PW50 000- - - Issued with gold Proof £5 Coin. Price new:		£895
RB5004	1999 (Jan)	**Merlyn Lowther (1999 - 2003):**		
		LNN (J01, K- - to M- -)		
		J01 - Originally for presentation packs only		£130
		K- -		£70
		M01		£150
		M- -		£90
RB5005		LLNN (LL- - replacement notes)		
		LL- -		£120

Reverse - Common to notes RB5001 to date

RB5006		**Andrew Bailey (2003 - Present):**		
		At the time of writing the Bank of England has not released any Bailey £50 notes into circulation.		

No.	Start date	Signature/face value/details	VF	EF	AUNC
		One Hundred Pounds - Large White Type			
		Design on one side only - 212 x 135mm - 8 5/16 x 5 5/16 in			
RB201		**C. P. Mahon (1925 - 1929):**			
			£700	£1,200	
RB202		**B. G. Catterns (1929 - 1934):**			
			£900	£1,800	
RB203		**K. O. Peppiatt (1934 - 1949):**			
		London	£700	£1,200	
		Liverpool	£800	£1,000	

RB203
Image courtesy of Pam West Banknotes.

No.	Start date	Signature/face value/details	VF	EF	AUNC

Two Hundred Pounds - Large White Type

Design on one side only.

RB220		**C. P. Mahon (1925 - 1929):**			
		SPECIMEN only		-	

Five Hundred Pounds - Large White Type

Design on one side only.

RB221		**C. P. Mahon (1925 - 1929):**			
			£5,000	£7,000	
RB222		**B. G. Catterns (1929 - 1934):**			
			£4,000	£6,000	
RB223		**K. O. Peppiatt (1934 - 1949):**			
			£4,000	£6,000	

Noted 2003, dated Sep 30th 1936, Liverpool £6,250

One Thousand Pounds - Large White Type

Design on one side only.

RB301		**C. P. Mahon (1925 - 1929):**			
			£6,000	£9,000	
RB302		**B. G. Catterns (1929 - 1934):**			
			£6,000	£9,000	
RB303		**K. O. Peppiatt (1934 - 1949):**			
			£10,000	£19,000	

Larger Denominations

In the past larger denomination notes have been produced, but none that were intended for circulation. Notable are the Fifteen Thousand Pound notes that were issued to British Airman in the 1991 Gulf War. The sum was paid to the airman on return. Very large denomination notes are also made by the Bank of England and issued to the note issuing banks of Scotland and Northern Ireland, so that the notes they circulate are always supported by the same amount in Bank of England sterling currency.

Appendix I. Comparative Catalogue Numbers for Treasury Notes

A Comparison table of the reference numbers in this book, and the two other most popular references for English banknotes.

CBN = This book, "Collectors' Bank Notes".
Duggleby = "English Paper Money" by V. Duggleby (6th edition used).
Pick = The "Standard Catalog of World Paper Money", originally by Albert Pick (The 10th edition (Vol. 2) and 9th edition (Vol. 3) were referred to).

CBN	Duggleby	Pick
	ONE SHILLING	
RT1	T23	-
RT2	T29	P353
	HALF CROWN	
RT3	T22	-
RT4	T28	P354
	FIVE SHILLINGS	
RT5	T21	P352
RT6	T27	P355
	TEN SHILLINGS	
RT7	T8	P346
RT8	T9	P346
RT8a	T9	P346
RT9	T10	P346
RT10	T12 Type 1	P348a
RT11	T12 Type 2	P348a
RT12	T12 Type 3	P348a
RT13	T13 Type 1	P348a
RT14	T13 Type 2	P348a
RT15	T15	P348b
RT16	T17	P350a
RT17	T18	P350a
RT18	T19	P350b
RT19	T20	P350b
RT20	T25	P356
RT21	T26	P356
RT22	T30	P358
RT23a	T33	P360
RT23b	T33a	P360

CBN	Duggleby	Pick
	ONE POUND	
RT25a	T1	P347
RT25b	T1	P347
RT25c	T1	P347
RT26a	T2	P347
RT26b	-	P347
RT26c	-	P347
RT27a	T3 Type 1	P347
RT27b	T3 Type 2	P347
RT27c	T3 Type 3	P347
RT27d	T3 Type 4	P347
RT28a	T4 Type 1	P347
RT28b	T4 Type 2	P347
RT29a	T5 Type 3	P347
RT29b	T5 Type 4	P347
RT30	T6	P347
RT31	T7	P347
RT32	T11 Type 1	P349a
RT33	T11 Type 2	P349a
RT34	T14	P349b
RT35	T16	P351
RT36	T24	P357
RT36a	T24	P357
RT37	T31	P359a
RT38	T32	P359b
RT39	T34	P361a
RT40	T35	P361b

Appendix II. Comparative Catalogue Numbers for Bank of England Notes

HALF CROWN

CBN	Duggleby	Pick
RB1	B254	P364

FIVE SHILLINGS

CBN	Duggleby	Pick
RB2	B253	P365

TEN SHILLINGS

CBN	Duggleby	Pick
RB3	B210	P362a
RBS3	B210s	-
RB5	B223	P362b
RBS5	B223s	-
RB7	B235	P362c
RBS7	B235s	-
RB8	B236	P362c
RB10	B251	P366
RBS10	B251s	-
RB12	B256	P362c
RBS12	B256s	-
RB14	B262	P368a
RB15	B263	P368a
RB16	B265	P368b
RB17	B266	P368b
RB18	B267	P368b
RB19	B271	P368c
RBS19	B271s	-
RB20	B272	P368c
RB21	B286	P373a
RBS21	B286s	-
RB22	B287	P373a
RB23	B294	P373b
RBS23	B294s	-
RB24	B295	P373b
RB25	B296	P373b
RB26	B309	P373c
RBS26	B309s	-
RB27	B310	P373c
RB28	B311	P373c

ONE POUND

CBN	Duggleby	Pick
RB31	B212	P363a
RBS31	B212s	-
RB33	B225	P363b
RBS33	B225s	-
RB34	B226	P363b
RB36	B238	P363c
RB37	B239	P363c
RB41	B248	P367a

ONE POUND (GUERNSEY O/P)

CBN	Duggleby	Pick
RBG31a	B212(A)	P363e
RBG33a	B225(A)	P363f
RBG34a	B226(A)	P363f
RBG36a	B238(A)	P363g
RBG37a	B239(A)	P363h
RBG37b	B239(B)	P363i
RBG37c	B239(C)	P363j
RBG41a	B248(A)	P367b
RBG42a	B249(A)	P367c

ONE POUND

CBN	Duggleby	Pick
RBS41	B?	
RB42	B249	P367a
RBS42	B249s	-
RB44	B258	P363d
RBS44	B258s	-
RB46	B260	P369a
RB47	B261	P369a
RB51	B268	P369b
RBS51	B268s	-
RB52	B269 - 261	P369b
RB53	B273	P369c
RBS53	B273s	-
RB54	B274	P369c
RB61	B281	P374a
RBS61	B281s	-
RB62	B282	P374a
RB63	B283	P374b
RB64	B284	P374a
RB65	B285	P374a
RB66	B288	P374c
RB67	B289	P374c
RB68	B290	P374c
RB69	B291	P374c
RB70	B292	P374d
RB71	B293	P374d
RB72	B301	P374e
RB73	B302	P374e
RB74	B303	P374f
RB75	B304	P374f
RB76	B305	P374e
RB77	B306	P374e
RB78	B307	P374f
RB79	B308	P374f
RB81a	B320	P374g
RB81b	B320	P374g
RB82	B321	P374g

ONE POUND

CBN	Duggleby	Pick
RB83	B322	P374g
RB84	B323	P374g
RB85	B337	P377a
RB86	B338	P377a
RB87	B339	P377a
RB87E	B339a	-
RB88	B340	P377a
RB89	B341	P377b
RB90	B342	P377b

FIVE POUNDS

CBN	Duggleby	Pick
RB101	B215	P320
RBS101	B215s	-
RB102	B228	P328
RBS102	B228s	-
RB103	B241	P335
RBS103	B241s	-
RB104	B255	P342
RBS104	B255s	-
RB105	B264	P343
RBS105	B264s	-
RB106	B270	P344
RBS106	B270s	-
RB107	B275	P345
RBS107	B275s	-
RB108	B276	P345
RB109	B277	P371
RBS109	B277s	-
RB110	B280	P372
RBS110	B280s	-
RB111	B297	P375a
RBS111	B297s	-
RB112	B298	P375a
RB113	B312	P375b
RBS113	B312s	-
RB114	B313	P375b
RB115	B314	P375b
RB116	B315	P375b
RB117	B324	P375c
RB118	B325	P375c
RB119	B332	P378a
RBS119	B332s	-
RB120	B333	P378a
RB121	B334	P378b
RBS121	B334s	-
RB122	B335	P378b
RB123	B336	P378b
RB124	B343	P378c

Appendix II. Comparative Catalogue Numbers for Bank of England Notes (continued)

FIVE POUNDS

CBN	Duggleby	Pick
RB126	B344	P378c
RB127	B345	P378d
RBS127	B345s	-
RB128	B353	P378e
RB501	B357	P382a/b
RB502	B362	P382c
RB503	B363	-
RB504	B364	-
RB504b	B365	-
RB505	C119	-
RB505b	C122a	-
RB505c	C123	-
RB505d	C126	-
RB506	C130	-
RB506b	C135	-
RB506c	C139	-
RB507	B378	-
RB508	B379	-
RB509	C149	-
RB510	C152	-
RB510b	C153	-
RB511	-	P392a/b
RB512	-	P392a/b
RB513	C160	-
RB514	C164	-
RB515	-	-

TEN POUNDS

CBN	Duggleby	Pick
RB151	B216	P321
RB152	B229	P329
RB153	B242	P336
RB154	B299	P376a
RBS154	B299s	-
RB156	B316	P376b
RBS156	B316s	-
RB158	B326	P376c
RBS158	B326s	-
RB159	B327	P376c
RB161	B330	P379a
RBS161	B330s	-
RB162	B331	P379a
RB163	B346	P379b
RB164	B347	P379b
RB165	B348	P379b
RB166	B349	P379c
RBS166	B349	-
RB167	B354	P379d
RB168	B360	P379e
RB1001	B366	P383
RB1002	B367	-
RB1003	B368	P386a
RB1003b	B369	P386a
RB1004	C120	CS3
RB1004b	C124	-
RB1004c	C127	-
RB1005	C131	-
RB1005b	C136	-
RB1006	B380	-
RB1006b	B381	-
RB1006c	C150	CS11
RB1006d	C154	-
RB1007	-	-
RB1007b	-	-
RB1008	-	-
RB1009	-	-
RB1010	C159	-
RB1010b	C161	-
RB1011	-	-

TWENTY POUNDS

CBN	Duggleby	Pick
RB171	B217	P322
RB172	B230	P330
RB173	B243	P337
RB174	B318	P380a
RBS174	B318s	-
RB175	B319	P380a
RB176	B328	P380b
RB177	B329	P380b
RB178	B350	P380c
RBS178	B350s	-
RB180	B351	P380d
RBS180	B351s	-
RB181	B355	P380e
RB2000	B358	P384a
RB2000b	B359	P384a
RB2001	-	-
RB2001b	-	-
RB2002	B370	P384b
RB2002b	B371	P384b
RB2003	B372	P387a
RB2003b	C128	-
RB2004	B373	P387a
RB2004b	B374	P387a
RB2005	B382	P387b
RB2006	-	-
RB2006b	-	-
RB2007	C151	-
RB2008	C155	-
RB2009	-	-
RB2010	C164	-
RB2011	-	-
RB2012	-	-

FIFTY POUNDS

CBN	Duggleby	Pick
RB191	B218	P323
RB192	B231	P331
RB193	B244	P338
RB194	B352	P381a
RBS194	B352s	-
RB195	B356	P381b
RB196	B361	P381c
RB5001	B375	P388a
RB5001b	B377	-
RB5002	-	-
RB5002b	-	-
RB5003	C132	-
RB5004	B383	P388b
RB5005	B384	-

ONE HUNDRED POUNDS

CBN	Duggleby	Pick
RB201	B219	P324
RB202	B232	P332
RB203	B245	P339

TWO HUNDRED POUNDS

CBN	Duggleby	Pick
RB220	B220	P325

FIVE HUNDRED POUNDS

CBN	Duggleby	Pick
RB221	B221	P326
RB222	B233	P333
RB223	B246	P340

ONE THOUSAND POUNDS

CBN	Duggleby	Pick
RB301	B222	P327
RB302	B234	P334
RB303	B247	P341

Bibliography - Suggested further reading

As Good As Gold - V Hewitt/J Keyworth, British Museum Publications.

Bank of England and Treasury Notes - D M Miller, Corbitt & Hunter.

Discovering Banknotes - K R Lake, Shire Publications.
ISBN 0852631650

English Paper Money - V Duggleby, Pam West (Publisher).
ISBN 0954345703

Nazi Counterfeiting of British Currency During WWII - B O Burke, Book Shop (Publisher). ISBN 0961827408

Promises to Pay - D Byatt/Bank of England, Spink and Son.
ISBN 0907605508

The Money Makers - W Kranister, Blackbear Publishing.

The Story of Money - Whitehead/Baskerville, Usborne Publishing.

The Story of Paper Money - Y Beresiner/C Narbeth, David & Charles Ltd. ISBN 0715357530

Standard Catalog of World Paper Money Vol 2, 10th Edition - A Pick/Various editiors. ISBN 087349704X

Standard Catalog of World Paper Money Vol 3, 9th Edition - A Pick/Various editors. ISBN 0873495918

Some Useful websites of Bank note Dealers etc

www.britishnotes.co.uk
www.thebanknotestore.com
www.collectpapermoney.co.uk
www.theIBNS.org (The International Bank Note Society)
www.banknotes4u.co.uk
www.colin-narbeth.com
www.worldnotes.co.uk
www.katespapermoney.com

For your Notes:

Many collectors like to keep a record of new notes that they purchase. The following four pages have been set aside for this purpose.

Ideal if you're equiped with your copy of Collectors' Banknotes, find yourself in a place selling banknotes and need to keep a record of what you've bought and for how much.

Some of the information worth recording would be:

Date	CBN Ref No.	Description	Cost	Seller

For your Notes:

Date	CBN Ref No.	Description	Cost	Seller

For your Notes:

Date	CBN Ref No.	Description	Cost	Seller

For your Notes:

Date	CBN Ref No.	Description	Cost	Seller